My Second Scene

Everything Adventurous, Fanciful, and Far Out

My Second Scene Book

Everything Adventurous, Fanciful, and Far Out

52 Scenes for Young Children

by Kristen Dabrowski

MY FIRST ACTING SERIES: VOLUME 5

A SMITH AND KRAUS BOOK • HANOVER, NEW HAMPSHIRE

A Smith and Kraus Book
Published by Smith and Kraus, Inc.
177 Lyme Road, Hanover, NH 03755
www.smithandkraus.com

First Edition: February 2009
Manufactured in the United States of America
9 8 7 6 5 4 3 2 1

ISBN-13: 978-1-57525-604-7 / ISBN-10 1-57525-604-5
Library of Congress Control Number: 2008927866

To my beautiful, wonderful mother,
who is sweet as a prune but not as wrinkled.
Thank you for all of your support
and imaginative assistance!

Contents

Foreword

Welcome to My First Acting Series! If you are not five to nine years old, PUT DOWN THIS BOOK! (OK, if you are a parent, guardian, teacher, agent, or someone who's just interested, you are welcome, too.)

In *My First Monologue Book*, we learned about what a monologue is and how to rehearse one. That book covered basic, everyday situations for kids like not wanting to go to bed, having to eat broccoli, and making new friends. If you haven't already seen it, check it out!

Now you know how to act like a kid your age, whether that boy or girl is nice, selfish, funny, smart—or all those things! *My Second Monologue Book* stretches your acting skills and your imagination even further. You can act out many historical, famous, and imaginary characters. This means you can play adults who do different jobs and come from different parts of the world.

My Third Monologue Book challenges your imagination and your brain! In this book, you act out characters in places far and near. Plus, you have to guess where the character is: In Egypt? Chicago? Oz? This book is very interactive. See what it's like to play detective!

A lot of kids will recognize situations in *My First Scene Book*. When do you listen to the rules? When do you break the rules? What are rules for? Why should you be polite? What do you do if other people don't act nicely? Discussion questions at the end of each scene help you think about what is happening and decide how you feel about the characters and situations.

In this book, you will put all these skills together---acting like a real kid, pretending to be someone famous or magical, being in strange or new places, acting with other people, and working on how to behave. *My Second Scene Book* is all about far out and imaginative people, places, and events! Live out your dreams! What is it like to live on the moon? Be a dragon? Battle a wizard? Prepare yourself for the adventure of your life as you put together all the skills in the previous books in this series!

Act out the characters for your family and friends. See if you can become this person with how you act and how you dress. Be creative! There's no wrong way to use this book. Dress up, have girls do boys' parts, make some of the girls into boys, write in the book, draw in the book, color the pictures—whatever you like! Feel free to ask adults and teachers for help with words you do not understand.

(NOTE: Parents and teachers, since these scenes are meant to be conversational, this book contains a lot of contractions and sentence fragments. It is a good opportunity to discuss what contractions are as well as the difference between formal language and conversational language. The goals of this book are primarily to sound realistic, provoke questions and opinions, create a unique acting volume, question morals and manners, and be a reading comprehension guide. Agents and managers, because the language in this book is highly conversational, it is a very good source for scenes that meet kids where they are now, developmentally.)

The last books in the series are *My First Acting Book*, which is all about how to be an actor, and a teacher's guide, complete with exercises and lesson plans. See how these books grow with you and your skills? Each book builds on the one before it.

- **Teachers:** Look for the teacher's guide to this series for many ideas about how to use this book in the classroom. This series can be used in reading, writing, drama, ethics, history, geography, and even science and math classes.
- **English/Drama Teachers and Parents:** There is also a guide to acting (*My First Acting Book*) with theater games, exercises, acting techniques, and information on how to be an actor.
- **Agents and Managers:** These scenes are immediate and active, with different emotions and levels. Great for auditions.

Enjoy and explore!

Kristen Dabrowski

Acting Lessons

1. A scene is any short play with more than one character.

2. When you are reading a scene out loud, think and talk like your character.

3. Try to understand how your character thinks and feels. This is very important! When you are an actor, you should behave just like your character.

4. Here are some examples of stage directions:

   (TERRY starts to run away.)

   (EMILY exits.)

   (GRANDMA gives RED a cookie.)

   (DRAGULA makes gobbling noises, then burps.)

   Stage directions are things the characters do in a scene. When you are reading a scene out loud, have someone play the narrator and read all the stage directions. When you are acting out a scene, you can just act out what the stage directions say.

5. When you perform a scene in front of an audience, make sure you speak loudly, so everyone can hear you.

6. When you perform a scene in front of an audience, pay attention to the other people onstage.

7. When you perform a scene in front of an audience, walk and dress like your character, too!

8. To memorize your lines (remember them without looking at the book), get a friend or a family member to say them with you over and over and over again.

9. If you are playing a character older or younger than you, think about how this might change how you think, walk, talk, and dress.

Part 1
SKITS FOR STARTERS

What are these characters saying?
Where are they?
You decide!

TRIP TO THE MOON

A lady visits the moon but does not like it.

Characters
　　Man
　　Lady

MAN: Welcome to the moon!

LADY: Thank you, sir.

MAN: Be careful of the craters, madam.

LADY: What is a crater?

MAN: It is a very big hole in the ground! If you fell in, it would be very hard to get out.

LADY: I thought the moon was made of cheese.

MAN: Cheese, madam? How very strange.

LADY: I flew all the way here to get some macaroni and moon cheese!

MAN: I am sorry, madam. I can make you a moon pie.

LADY: No, I do not like pie.

MAN: Do not like pie!

LADY: I do not like circles or triangles.

MAN: I see. I must tell you, madam, that the moon is a circle.

LADY: Oh my! I do not like the moon at all! Send me back to the earth!

MAN: The earth is round, too!

LADY: Send me somewhere square!

MAN: Our library here on the moon is very square.

LADY: Then that will do.

MAN: Thank you for visiting the moon!

Questions

1. Would you like to visit the moon? Why or why not?

2. Do you have a favorite shape?

3. What do you know about the moon?

4. Write down one fact about the moon that the Lady does not know.

THE SEA IS FOR ME

Nick wants to sail off on the sea!

Characters

Nick
Lily
Tim
Ellie
Captain Jon

NICK: Today is the day I go to sea!

LILY: Why do you want to go to sea?

NICK: The sea is the best place for me!

TIM: Why not live in a tree?

NICK: The tree is not where I want to be.

CAPTAIN JON: Get aboard, quick!

ELLIE: The clock goes tick-tick!

LILY: Why are we speaking in rhyme?

TIM: It's not a crime.

CAPTAIN JON: We're running out of time!

NICK: Aboard I will climb. *(Climbs on the ship.)*
    I'm free! I'm free!

ELLIE: You're out on the sea!

TIM: Farewell, Nick!

LILY: Farewell, Nick!

ELLIE: Farewell, Nick!

NICK: Someone get a bucket, I'm about to be sick!

Questions

1. What words can you think of that rhyme with "sea"?

2. Do you think Nick will stay on the ship?

3. Why do you think Nick wants to be out on the sea?

4. Draw a picture of Nick's adventures.

THE RHYMING BUG

A rhyming bug bites Tommy.

Characters

Tommy

Momma

TOMMY: A nasty rhyming bug just bit me on my nose! *(He shudders and frowns.)* I feel nasty and rhyme-y right down to my toes.

MOMMA: Tommy, it's dinnertime—your favorite, meatballs and spaghetti.

TOMMY: I don't feel like eating dinner! I'll come when I'm ready.

MOMMA: If you know what's good for you . . .

TOMMY: I'll stand here 'til I'm blue!

MOMMA: Stop that back-talking right away.

TOMMY: I won't obey, NO MATTER WHAT YOU SAY!

MOMMA: Come in for dinner and stop being whiney.

TOMMY: I feel buggy and nasty and grimy and rhyme-y!

MOMMA: *(To the audience as TOMMY listens in.)* He must have been bitten by a nasty rhyme-y bug. This isn't the way my Tommy behaves. I'll just say something that he can't rhyme, and the nasty rhyme-y bug's spell will be broken. *(To Tommy.)* Did a nasty rhyme-y bug bite you? That's worse than being stung by a bee!

TOMMY: I can rhyme anything, so your stupid plan won't work on me.

(MOMMA tries to think of something TOMMY can't rhyme. She suddenly thinks of something!)

MOMMA: Tommy, since you don't want dinner, would you like an orange?

TOMMY: Just leave me alone! I'm feeling . . . *(TOMMY thinks.)* I'm feeling . . . Let's see . . . borange? That's not a word. I'm feeling . . . dorange? That's not a word either! Orange, forange, porange, lorange?

(TOMMY thinks.)

TOMMY: Hey, Momma, I can't rhyme anything with orange. And I'm feeling better! Oh boy, meatballs and spaghetti for dinner. I can't wait to eat it up!

(MOMMA jumps back and rubs her nose.)

MOMMA: *(In a nasty voice.)* Hold your horses, sonny, now I have to heat it up.

Questions

1. Do you think there are really nasty rhyme-y bugs?

2. Can you think of a good thing to say to Momma to break the nasty rhyme-y bug's spell on her?

3. Do you ever feel nasty for no special reason? What do you do to feel better again?

4. Can you rhyme some words?

   Rat rhymes with _____.

   More rhymes with _____.

   Cheese rhymes with _____.

5. Can you finish this poem with rhyming words?

   I met a rat wore a great _____. Upon my favorite chair he _____.

   "That's my chair," I said. "Please sit on the floor."

   I gave him some cheese, then he wanted some

   _____.

   He said, "Give me more of that cheese!"

   I said, "Only if you say _____!"

TERRY AND THE TIGERS

Terry encounters two tigers.

Characters

Narrator 1
Narrator 2
Narrator 3
Narrator 4
Narrator 5
Narrator 6
Terry
Sasha
Rajah

NARRATOR 1: Let us tell you a story—

NARRATOR 2: —about bravery—

NARRATOR 3: —and danger—

NARRATOR 4: —and tigers, too.

NARRATOR 5: It starts right here—

NARRATOR 6: —under this circus tent.

NARRATOR 1: The circus is quiet now.

NARRATOR 2: Everyone is asleep.

NARRATOR 3: Everyone but Terry.

(TERRY enters.)

NARRATOR 4: Terry is all alone in this big circus world.

NARRATOR 5: Terry has no mother.

NARRATOR 6: Terry has no father.

NARRATORS 1/2/3: Terry has no sister.

NARRATORS 4/5/6: Terry has no brother.

TERRY: I wish I had a friend in this big circus world. Anyone will do.

ALL NARRATORS: Anyone?

(SASHA and RAJAH, two tigers, enter looking sad.)

SASHA: Who is this?

(TERRY starts to run away.)

RAJAH: Wait! Don't run away!

SASHA: Is that Terry?

TERRY: Yes.

RAJAH: Would you like to play?

TERRY: Do tigers like to play with children?

SASHA/RAJAH: Yes, we do!

NARRATOR 1: I'm not sure these tigers are nice.

NARRATOR 2: Don't listen to them, Terry!

NARRATOR 3: Tigers are mean.

TERRY: Are you sure you want to play with me?

SASHA: This child is frightened, Rajah.

RAJAH: Why, Sasha? We are being sweet.

NARRATOR 4: Tigers are terrible!

NARRATOR 5: Big cats are cruel.

NARRATOR 6: Felines are ferocious and rotten—

ALL NARRATORS: —and drool!

TERRY: I heard that tigers can be—

SASHA/RAJAH: What?

TERRY: You are a little scary.

SASHA/RAJAH: Why?

TERRY: You have big teeth and claws, and you are very, very hairy.

SASHA: We can't help how we look.

TERRY: That is true.

RAJAH: We always try to be kind to you.

SASHA: Don't you see, Terry?

RAJAH: We are just like you.

SASHA/RAJAH: We have trouble making friends, too!

TERRY: That does seem to be true.

SASHA: Everyone is afraid of us.

RAJAH: And we want to have more friends!

SASHA: We could have such fun, Terry!

RAJAH: You could race on our backs!

SASHA: We could play hide and seek!

RAJAH: We could tell stories while the others are asleep.

SASHA: But are you brave enough?

RAJAH: Do you believe what we say is true?

(TERRY thinks. The NARRATORS lean in to hear his answer.)

TERRY: I do. I will be brave and be friends with you!

NARRATOR 1: Then something strange happened—

NARRATOR 2: —strange but true!

NARRATOR 3: They sat and told stories 'til quarter to two!

NARRATOR 4: Terry learned a lesson that day.

NARRATOR 5: Sometimes to make new friends—

NARRATOR 6: —you must not be scared—

NARRATORS 1/2/3: Do not run away—

NARRATORS 4/5/6: —maybe the others feel the same way!

(RAJAH, SASHA, and TERRY step forward.)

RAJAH: Now our tale is at an end.

TERRY: Don't you mean your tails are on your ends?

SASHA: Terry, I think we will always be friends.

ALL: The end!

Questions

1. Do you think Terry and the tigers will be friends?

2. Do you think the tigers are nice or mean? Why?

3. Is it scary to try to make new friends? Why?

4. Do you have any ideas to help someone who is trying to make friends?

5. What can you do to help someone who is new at school?

6. What makes someone your friend?

7. Do you ever think someone is nice or mean because of how they look? Is this smart or unfair?

8. Which words in this scene rhyme?

JACK AND THE MAGIC BEANS

Jack brings magic beans home to his mother.

Characters

Jack
Mother

JACK: Mother, I have some magic beans!

MOTHER: Jack, I told you to buy a cow, not beans!

JACK: But these beans are magic.

MOTHER: They just look like plain old beans to me. I will cook them.

JACK: Mother, no!

(MOTHER puts the beans in a pot and stirs them with a spoon.)

MOTHER: These beans are all we have to eat.

JACK: If we planted those beans, we could grow many, many beans!

MOTHER: We need to eat now, silly boy. Here are your beans.

(MOTHER feeds JACK the beans.)

JACK: Mother, I feel . . . funny.

MOTHER: What is wrong with you, Jack?

JACK: I think these are Mexican jumping beans!

(JACK starts to jump up and down and dance.)

MOTHER: What are you doing, Jack?

JACK: I am jumping and dancing!

MOTHER: That is very unusual.

JACK: Mother, I just had an idea!

MOTHER: What is your idea, Jack?

JACK: I will go into town and become a performer!

MOTHER: Oh, Jack. Actors don't make money.

JACK: I will dance and sing!

MOTHER: Oh. Well, that's OK then.

JACK: I told you those beans were magic!

Questions

1. What would you do if you bought magic beans? Would you cook them? Would you eat them? Would you plant them?

2. What other things do you think the magic beans can do?

3. Do you think the magic beans make Jack a better dancer?

4. How do you think Jack should dance after he eats the magic beans?

5. How should his mother talk, walk, and act?

Part 2

CLASSIC TALES
(with a twist)

What are these characters saying?
Where are they?
You decide!

RED RIDING HOODIE

The Wolf mistakes Red for a girl.

Characters

Red
Wolf
Grandma

Onstage, RED (a boy) looks all around him. He is lost. He is wearing a red hoodie, and the hood is up.

WOLF: Hello, little girl.

RED: I'm not a girl.

WOLF: That's what they all say.

RED: I'm not a girl!

WOLF: You're wearing a red riding hood.

RED: I'm wearing a red hoodie.

WOLF: Right. A red riding hood.

RED: Sort of. So what?

WOLF: So, all the delicious little girls wear red riding hoods. It's in all the books. *(Pulls out a book.)* See? *How to Eat Delicious Little Girls* by Wolf Wolfingham. Chapter one: "The most delicious little girls always wear red riding hoods."

RED: That book doesn't make any sense. Why would wearing a red hood make you more delicious?

WOLF: Wolf Wolfingham is a doctor. He studied at Howl University in the Black Hills. He knows.

RED: Well, I think that's a silly idea.

WOLF: It doesn't matter what you think because I am going to eat you now, little girl.

RED: I'm not a little girl!

WOLF: Then why are you wearing a red riding hood?

RED: I'm wearing a hoodie. A sweatshirt with a hood.

(GRANDMA enters.)

GRANDMA: Red! Where are you?

RED: I'm here, Grandma. There's a really dumb wolf out here.

WOLF: I am not dumb!

RED: He thinks girls who wear red hoods taste the best, and he thinks I'm a girl!

GRANDMA: Why does he think you're a girl?

RED: Why do you think I'm a girl?

WOLF: Because you're wearing a red hood!

RED: That doesn't make sense.

WOLF: You say that too much. Maybe you don't know what sense is.

RED: Maybe you don't!

GRANDMA: Take it easy, children. Don't fight.

WOLF: He started it.

RED: He wants to eat me, Grandma! We should kill him.

GRANDMA: Now don't be hasty. We can work this out with words.

WOLF: But I'm hungry now.

RED: Go find yourself some stinky girl to eat.

WOLF: But you're wearing a—

RED: A hoodie! A hoodie! Not a red riding hood!

WOLF: Close enough!

RED: He wants to eat me, Grandma! Please can we kill him?

GRANDMA: Enough about killing and eating. We are going to work this out like nice young men.

WOLF: I'm a wolf.

RED: And I'm a boy.

GRANDMA: So you don't even want to try to work this out in a polite way?

WOLF/RED: No!

GRANDMA: Then I guess I'll have to eat all of the cookies myself . . .

RED: Cookies?

GRANDMA: Your favorite—chocolate chip!

RED: I could maybe try to be nicer.

GRANDMA: And you, Wolf? What do you say?

WOLF: What's a cookie?

RED: You don't know what a cookie is?

GRANDMA: *(Handing WOLF a cookie.)* Here you go.

(WOLF puts the cookie in his mouth in one big bite. His eyes get big, his feet dance, and his fingers wiggle as he chews.)

GRANDMA: Do you like it?

RED: Can I have one, too?

(As GRANDMA hands RED a cookie, WOLF finishes chewing.)

WOLF: Wowee, wowee, wow! That was a . . . cookie?

GRANDMA: That's right, young man. A cookie.

WOLF: That tasted better than any little girl I've ever eaten! Why didn't I know about these cookies sooner? Why didn't Doctor Wolfingham tell me about cookies? Can I have another?

GRANDMA: May I have another?

WOLF: You made them. You can have another if you want to.

RED: She wants you to say, "May I have another?"

WOLF: Why?

RED: Because maybe you can have another, but you may not.

WOLF: What?

RED: It's more polite to say "may I" than it is to say "can I."

WOLF: This is why we eat people. You talk too much. Give me another cookie or I'll eat this red riding hoodie, Grandma!

GRANDMA: Rude little wolves don't get any cookies. Now you take a time out until you can behave nicely.

(WOLF stands still.)

GRANDMA: Go on. Go stand over there until you can be nice.

(WOLF takes a few steps to the left.)

GRANDMA: Good. You think about what you did.

RED: Grandma, may I have a cookie?

GRANDMA: Of course you may, Red.

(GRANDMA gives RED a cookie.)

WOLF: No fair.

RED: Mmmmm. Grandma, may I have another cookie?

GRANDMA: OK. Just one more. *(Handing over another cookie.)*

RED: Thank you, Grandma!

WOLF: I want a cookie!

GRANDMA: Do you have something you'd like to say, Mister Wolf?

WOLF: Mmmmmay I have a cookie? Or two— he got two!

GRANDMA: What's the magic word?

WOLF: I thought I said the magic word!

RED: She wants you to say "please."

WOLF: Fine! Pleeeeease mmmmmay I have two more cookies?

GRANDMA: Since you asked so nicely, you may have two more cookies. *(Hands WOLF two cookies.)* Now isn't this better than fighting?

RED: Maybe.

WOLF: I still might eat you later.

RED: I still won't be a girl later.

GRANDMA: That's enough. You boys play nice or there won't be any more cookies later.

WOLF/RED: OK.

Questions

1. How can you act and look like a wolf?

2. Why does Grandma want the Wolf to say "may I"?

3. Is politeness important? Why or why not?

4. Do you think Wolf will want to eat Red later?

5. Why does Wolf listen to Grandma?

THE PICKY WOLF

This wolf will not try any new foods.

Characters

Wolf
Red
Hunter

A little girl, RED, steps onto the stage.
WOLF hides behind a tree.

WOLF: Oh, little girl . . .

RED: What?

WOLF: Wouldn't you like to step off the path?

RED: No.

WOLF: Why not? There are pretty flowers here you can take to your granny.

RED: Nah. Don't want to.

WOLF: Oh, come on.

RED: You'll eat me.

WOLF: I can eat you on the path, too.

RED: That's against the rules.

WOLF: So? I could do it anyway.

RED: Well maybe I'd shoot you.

WOLF: Shoot me? There's no need for violence.

RED: You said you were going to eat me.

WOLF: So?

RED: So don't you think that will be violent?

WOLF: No.

RED: You think I'll just sit there and let you eat me?

WOLF: You look like a nice girl.

RED: I'm not going to let you eat me.

WOLF: I see. We do have a problem.

RED: Why don't you eat plants and flowers and nuts and berries? We're in the forest.

WOLF: I don't like them.

RED: You're a picky eater.

WOLF: I know.

RED: You only like to eat little girls?

WOLF: Or boys. Or rabbits.

RED: Rabbits are sweet! You mustn't eat rabbits.

WOLF: But I can eat boys?

RED: Well . . . I guess you shouldn't.

WOLF: I'm hungry! I have to eat something.

RED: I have an idea! You could eat my toenails. They are getting a bit long. I could cut them and give them to you.

WOLF: Oooo! Yes, please!

(RED pretends to cut her toenails and give them to WOLF.)

WOLF: Ewww! They taste like soft-shell crabs.

(HUNTER enters.)

HUNTER: Ah-ha! Don't worry, little girl! I will save you. I shall hit this wolf with my ax and cut him in half.

WOLF: Ahhh!

RED: Wait a second.

HUNTER: What?

WOLF: No violence—please!

HUNTER: But you are a wolf, and I am a hunter!

RED: Do hunters use axes?

HUNTER: No, not usually.

RED: I think this wolf just needs to try new foods.

WOLF: I hate new foods!

RED: You just need to try them. You might be surprised.

WOLF: I won't be surprised. I don't like to eat anything except little girls.

HUNTER: Have you ever had falafel?

WOLF: Fa-what-el?

HUNTER: Fa-la-fel! It's made of chickpeas!

WOLF: Peas? Yech!

RED: What about peanut butter and jelly?

WOLF: Sounds messy.

RED: It's a sandwich. You put the peanut butter and jelly on bread.

WOLF: Hm. Maybe.

RED: I like my sandwiches with extra, extra, extra peanut butter. I have one in my basket. Want to try it?

WOLF: Well . . . OK.

(RED hands WOLF a sandwich. WOLF eats the sandwich, which has lots and lots of peanut butter and is very sticky.)

WOLF: Nad gump fradit.

HUNTER: What?

RED: Quick! His mouth is too sticky with peanut butter to eat us! Let's run away!

HUNTER: But I wanted to hit him with an ax.

RED: Don't be silly! Let's go!

(HUNTER and RED run away. WOLF gets very angry and throws a temper tantrum until he finally swallows all of the peanut butter.)

WOLF: Ooooo, I'll get you yet! Mmmmm. I do like that peanut butter, though . . . And it's only a little bit violent to eat. Tasty! *(Shouting as he exits.)* Oh, little girl! Do you have another sandwich?

Questions

1. Do you like to try new foods?

2. Why is it hard to try new foods?

3. Who is your favorite character and why?

4. How can you make an empty stage seem like the deep, dark woods?

CINDERELLA

A Pick-an-Adventure Play.

THE BEGINNING: AT THE BALL

The stepsisters arrive at the ball.

Characters
Wilhemina
Stepmother
Drucilla

WILHEMINA: It's beautiful!

STEPMOTHER: Stop gawking, Wilhemina!

WILHEMINA: Sorry, Mother.

DRUCILLA: Are we the loveliest girls here, Mother?

STEPMOTHER: Of course you are, Drucilla.

DRUCILLA: Do you really think the Prince will fall in love with us?

STEPMOTHER: Of course he will.

WILHEMINA: I'm not sure I'm ready for marriage, Mother.

STEPMOTHER: Don't talk nonsense, Wilhemina! He is a prince! Everyone wants to marry him.

WILHEMINA: Maybe he's ugly.

DRUCILLA: Maybe you're ugly.

STEPMOTHER: Girls! Behave! Now where is that Prince? Daughters, look for that Prince.

WILHEMINA: How will who he is?

STEPMOTHER: He will look like a prince!

WILHEMINA: Everyone is dressed up. All the men look like princes.

DRUCILLA: You really are a dunce, Willie. The Prince will be the handsomest one here!

WILHEMINA: *(Pointing.)* He's handsome.

DRUCILLA: He's a waiter! The Prince is sure to fall in love with me. Not only am I prettier than you, I'm smarter, too. *(Pointing.)* That is the Prince.

WILHEMINA: That is a statue.

DRUCILLA: No, it isn't!

WILHEMINA: Dru, it's made of stone, and it's wrestling a tiger!

DRUCILLA: The Prince sure is brave.

STEPMOTHER: You nincompoops, the Prince is the one wearing a crown on the throne over there! Now let's go talk to him. And you behave yourselves!

Pick an Adventure!

What happens next? You decide on the ending!
Choose which scene ends the story.

Ending 1: The Prince falls in love with one of the
stepsisters. For this ending, go to page 35.

Ending 2: The Prince doesn't want to get married.
For this ending, go to page 37.

Ending 3: The Prince turns into a wolf. For this
ending, go to page 41.

Ending 4: The Prince breaks her glass slippers,
and Cinderella has to go to the hospital. For this
ending, go to page 45.

Want another ending? Draw or write it here!

ENDING 1: LOVE, LOVE, LOVE

The Prince loves the stepsisters' honesty.

Characters
Drucilla
Wilhemina
Stepmother
Prince

DRUCILLA: Yoo-hoo! Princie!

WILHEMINA: I think I might be sick.

STEPMOTHER: Your Majesty, may I present my beautiful daughters, Drucilla and Wilhemina.

PRINCE: Pleased to meet you.

DRUCILLA: You sure are handsome.

WILHEMINA: My dress itches.

PRINCE: It's nice to meet girls who are so honest!

WILHEMINA: I don't like to take baths.

DRUCILLA: I want to marry you because you are rich, and I want lots of diamonds.

STEPMOTHER: Be quiet!

PRINCE: No, no! Go on! I love honesty. It's one of the best traits a person can have.

WILHEMINA: I bite my toenails.

DRUCILLA: I want to live in this castle and have servants do everything for me!

PRINCE: Stop, stop!

STEPMOTHER: I told you to be quiet, little fools!

PRINCE: I have chosen my wife! She shall be . . . Wilhemina! You are the most honest girl in the kingdom!

Questions

1. Do you think honesty is a good quality?

2. Do you think the Prince and Wilhemina will be happy together?

3. Do you like to take baths? Why or why not?

4. What do you think Wilhemina and Drucilla look like?

ENDING 2: THANKS, BUT NO THANKS

The Prince does not want to get married.

Characters

Stepmother
Prince
Cinderella
Drucilla
Wilhemina

STEPMOTHER: Prince, may I present my
daughters, the charming Wilhemina and the
lovely Drucilla.

PRINCE: Greetings, ladies.

(CINDERELLA appears.)

CINDERELLA: You forgot me, Stepmother.

STEPMOTHER: Where did you come from? I
thought I told you not to come to the ball until
you did all of your chores!

CINDERELLA: I finished my chores.

STEPMOTHER: Impossible!

DRUCILLA: Impossible!

WILHEMINA: Impossible, Cindersmella!

CINDERELLA: Please don't call me that!

STEPMOTHER: Horrible child! Go home at once!

PRINCE: She is here now. Let's all just try to have a good time. It is a ball, after all!

WILHEMINA: That rhymes!

DRUCILLA: You're a poet, and you don't even know it.

WILHEMINA: That rhymes, too!

DRUCILLA: Duuuh.

STEPMOTHER: Stand up straight, Cinderella!

PRINCE: Excuse me, but there are other ladies waiting to meet me. Could you fight over there?

CINDERELLA: Your Highness, would you . . . like to dance?

PRINCE: Nah.

CINDERELLA: But . . . my fairy godmother said . . . I thought . . .

PRINCE: That I'd fall in love with you?

CINDERELLA: Well, it's more than I could hope for, but—

PRINCE: That's what all the girls think.

STEPMOTHER: But I thought this ball was for you to find your Princess!

PRINCE: That's what my dad wants me to do.

DRUCILLA: What do you want?

PRINCE: I want to hunt and play games and do whatever I want. And I don't want to get married.

WILHEMINA: Can we go home now, Mama? This dress is really itchy. I hate it.

STEPMOTHER: Hush, silly child! I guess we must go home then. Some prince you are!

PRINCE: Whatever.

STEPMOTHER: Come, Cinderella. There are more chores to do at home.

CINDERELLA: But—but—this was supposed to be my way out! Prince, you were supposed to set me free from the clutches of my evil stepmother!

PRINCE: She seems OK.

CINDERELLA: She makes me do chores all the time!

PRINCE: My mom tries to get me to clean my room, too. I pay one of the servants to do it.

CINDERELLA: But you don't understand! You're supposed to save me!

PRINCE: I guess you'll just have to save yourself.

CINDERELLA: Save myself? But how?

Questions

1. What can Cinderella do to save herself besides marrying the Prince?

2. How is this Prince different from most fairy tale princes? Do you like him better or worse than the other princes? Why?

3. If I had a fairy godmother, I'd ask her to help me with _____

   _____.

ENDING 3: THE PRINCE CHANGES

The Prince has a secret: He's a werewolf!

Characters

Drucilla
Stepmother
Prince
Cinderella
Wilhemina

DRUCILLA: Oh look! The moon just came up!
A full moon.

STEPMOTHER: Isn't that romantic, Prince?

PRINCE: A full moon? No! *(Hides behind his
throne.)*

(CINDERELLA enters quickly.)

CINDERELLA: Prince? Is something wrong?

DRUCILLA: Aaaaaaaah!!! He's a wolf! Not a prince
at all!

WILHEMINA: Aw. Aren't you cute?

*(The PRINCE comes out from behind the
throne. He is hairy, like a wolf.)*

PRINCE: Shhh! Not so loud!

STEPMOTHER: Oh my goodness! You're a monster!

PRINCE: No! I'm just . . . a werewolf. It runs in the family every fourth generation. It's a secret.

CINDERELLA: That's terrible!

WILHEMINA: Are you house-trained?

PRINCE: Of course! I'm a prince!

WILHEMINA: Mom, can we take him home?

DRUCILLA: No, Mommy! He's icky.

STEPMOTHER: If you take him home, you have to walk him and feed him and take care of him.

DRUCILLA: I don't want a dog!

PRINCE: I'm a werewolf!

WILHEMINA: Pleeease, can we take him home? I promise Cinderella will take care of him.

CINDERELLA: Does it hurt?

PRINCE: Does what hurt?

CINDERELLA: Changing into a wolf?

PRINCE: No, it's just embarrassing.

CINDERELLA: You're just a little hairy, that's all. You still seem perfectly nice.

PRINCE: I am hungry for raw meat.

DRUCILLA: Ewww! Icky!

WILHEMINA: Pleeeeeeeeease, Mommy?

STEPMOTHER: Very well, Wilhemina. We will take the Prince home with us.

PRINCE: Wait a minute! I don't think I want to go with you!

WILHEMINA: I'm going to call him Woofy.

PRINCE: My name is William!

STEPMOTHER: Let's go!

DRUCILLA: If she gets a wolf, I want a—a—Prince!

STEPMOTHER: Girls, girls, you can share him. Drucilla, you will get the Prince. Wilhemina, you will get the wolf.

CINDERELLA: What do I get?

STEPMOTHER: A lot more housework. Come on; let's go home!

CINDERELLA: Where's my fairy godmother when I need her?

Questions

1. In a play, how can you make the Prince change from a human to a werewolf?

2. Show the class how you can look like you are changing into a werewolf!

3. Should Wilhemina have to take care of the werewolf without Cinderella's help?

4. Write three words that describe each character:

   Wilhemina: _____, _____, and _____.

   Drucilla: _____, _____, and _____.

   Cinderella: _____, _____, and _____.

   Prince: _____, _____, and _____.

   Stepmother: _____, _____, and _____.

ENDING 4: CINDERELLA GOES TO THE HOSPITAL

Cinderella has a little accident at the ball. (Never wear glass shoes!)

Characters

Cinderella
Stepmother
Prince
Drucilla
Wilhemina
Fairy Godmother

CINDERELLA: Hello, Stepmother.

STEPMOTHER: I thought I left you at home!

CINDERELLA: You did, but I finished my chores—

PRINCE: Who is this lovely creature?

DRUCILLA: No one.

WILHEMINA: Just some old relative of ours.

DRUCILLA: Shhh! You're not supposed to tell people that!

STEPMOTHER: She is a complete stranger. I've never seen her before.

PRINCE: She's wonderful.

WILHEMINA: She's just a girl.

PRINCE: Will you dance with me?

CINDERELLA: OK. What is your name?

PRINCE: The Prince.

CINDERELLA: Don't you have another name?

PRINCE: Yes. My name is Hunkferd.

CINDERELLA: Hunkferd? I think I'll call you Prince.

PRINCE: OK. Shall we dance?

CINDERELLA: Yes, let's!

(CINDERELLA and the PRINCE start to dance. He is a very bad dancer and steps on CINDERELLA's toes.)

CINDERELLA: Ouch!

PRINCE: I'm sorry!

CINDERELLA: It's all right. You didn't mean to— ouch!

PRINCE: Forgive me. My mother tried to make me go to dance lessons—

CINDERELLA: You broke my glass slippers!

PRINCE: I'll buy you new slippers.

CINDERELLA: No, you don't understand! My slippers were made of glass! When they broke, they cut my feet.

PRINCE: Oh no!

DRUCILLA: Gross!

WILHEMINA: Cool!

PRINCE: Quick! This girl must get to the hospital!

(The PRINCE exits.)

STEPMOTHER: Well we can't take her home like this.

CINDERELLA: My fairy godmother will help me. Help me, fairy godmother!

DRUCILLA: You have a fairy godmother?

CINDERELLA: Doesn't everyone?

(The FAIRY GODMOTHER appears.)

FAIRY GODMOTHER: You called me, dear?

CINDERELLA: I need to get to the hospital. The glass slippers cut my feet!

FAIRY GODMOTHER: I'm afraid I don't know the way to the hospital.

CINDERELLA: Can you fix my feet? I think I need stitches.

FAIRY GODMOTHER: I'm a fairy godmother, not a doctor, dear. If you want mice turned into a motorboat, I'd be happy to help.

WILHEMINA: I've always wanted a motorboat.

(The PRINCE enters.)

PRINCE: Quick! There is a carriage outside to take you to the hospital!

CINDERELLA: Thank you! Oh, what a magical night—except for cutting my feet and having to go to the hospital.

FAIRY GODMOTHER: Let me help you outside, dear girl.

(CINDERELLA and the FAIRY GODMOTHER exit.)

PRINCE: Oh no! I don't even know her name! Who was that lovely lady?

WILHEMINA: Her name is Blecky Bleckinger.

DRUCILLA: She doesn't have a name.

STEPMOTHER: I can't remember.

PRINCE: I will take this slipper to every house in the kingdom. I must find out who owns this slipper!

(The PRINCE bends down to pick up the broken slipper.)

PRINCE: Ouch! Oh no! I cut myself on these glass slippers! I must go to the hospital.

DRUCILLA: The same hospital that Cinder—I mean, that strange girl went to?

PRINCE: Yes! Yes! That is how I will find her! I will meet her at the hospital. I must go!

(The PRINCE exits in a hurry.)

DRUCILLA: Mother, this was not a nice ball.

WILHEMINA: Are you kidding? This was the most exciting ball ever!

Questions

1. Would the Prince be a good husband for Cinderella?

2. Would you want glass shoes? Why or why not?

3. Imagine that you are at this ball. What would you do? Who would you talk to?

GOLDILOCKS

A Pick-an-Adventure Play.

THE BEGINNING: THE BREAK-IN

Goldilocks arrives the bears' house.

Characters
Goldie
Lexie
Emily
Baby Bear
Mama Bear
Papa Bear

GOLDIE: I'm hungry. Let's go into this house!

LEXIE: I don't think that's a good idea. We don't know who lives here!

GOLDIE: They won't care. I'll just eat a little bit.

EMILY: You're not supposed to go into strangers' houses!

GOLDIE: You worry too much. Come on!

(GOLDIE walks in.)

GOLDIE: This is a pretty nice house.

LEXIE: Everything is kind of big.

EMILY: Oh, Goldie. I don't think we should be here!

GOLDIE: Don't be a chicken.

LEXIE: Bear.

GOLDIE: "Don't be a bear"? That doesn't make any sense.

LEXIE: No. Bear. In the picture.

(GOLDIE picks up a picture frame.)

GOLDIE: It is a bear.

EMILY: We gotta get out of here—now!

GOLDIE: I haven't had anything to eat yet. I'm hungry!

EMILY: I'm going home.

GOLDIE: You're a chicken, Emily.

EMILY: I don't care. I like chickens! I'm scared of bears!

(EMILY exits.)

LEXIE: I think Emily might be right, Goldie.

GOLDIE: We're already in here. We're just going to have a little bit to eat so I don't starve to death, then we'll go. Bears probably have LOTS of food. They won't even miss it!

LEXIE: Well . . .

GOLDIE: Look! Here is a breakfast all set up for us! Ick. It's just porridge. Come on; let's eat!

LEXIE: No, you eat without me.

GOLDIE: Don't you want any?

LEXIE: Um, I'm not really hungry.

GOLDIE: OK. More food for me!

(GOLDIE eats the porridge.)

LEXIE: Can we go now?

GOLDIE: One bowl of porridge was too hot, one was too cold, and one was just right.

LEXIE: But you ate them all anyway.

GOLDIE: I was hungry. I'm sleepy now.

LEXIE: The bears are going to come back any minute! They probably wanted the breakfast!

GOLDIE: They can make another breakfast.

LEXIE: Maybe they'll make us their new breakfast!

GOLDIE: Don't be silly, Lexie. There's lots of food here.

LEXIE: Let's go home.

GOLDIE: I'm going to take a nap.

LEXIE: Are you crazy? You broke into a bear family's house, ate their food, and now you're going to sleep in their beds?

GOLDIE: Not all of the beds. Just one bed.

LEXIE: I'm going home.

GOLDIE: See you later.

LEXIE: Come on, Goldie! Come with me!

GOLDIE: Nope. I'm gonna take a nap.

(LEXIE leaves. GOLDIE sits on one bed.)

GOLDIE: Ugh! This bed is too hard, like sleeping on a wooden floor.

(GOLDIE sits on another bed.)

GOLDIE: This bed is too soft. It feels like a wet cloud.

(GOLDIE sits the last bed.)

GOLDIE: This bed is juuuuust right!

(GOLDIE settles down to sleep. Just then, three bears enter: MAMA, PAPA, and BABY BEAR.)

Questions

1. What do you think of Goldie? Would you be her friend?

2. Would you leave or stay in the house?

3. Would you go into a stranger's home?

4. How do you think the bears will react to seeing Goldie in their house?

Pick an Adventure!

What happens next? You decide on the ending! Choose which scene ends the story.

Ending 1: The bears call the police. For this ending, go to page 55.

Ending 2: The bears adopt Goldie. For this ending, go to page 60.

Want another ending? Draw or write it here!

ENDING 1: EEEK! A GIRL!

The bears call the police.

Characters

Baby Bear
Mama Bear
Papa Bear
Goldie
Officer Ben
Goldie's Mom
Goldie's Dad
Lexie
Emily

BABY BEAR: Mama, Papa, there's someone in my bed!

MAMA BEAR: Who is it?

PAPA BEAR: This bear has no hair!

BABY BEAR: I'm scared!

MAMA BEAR: Let's call the police!

PAPA BEAR: Quiet! We must not wake this scary, bald bear.

(GOLDIE yawns and turns over in her sleep. MAMA, PAPA, and BABY BEAR scream. GOLDIE wakes up.)

GOLDIE: Bears!

PAPA BEAR: Don't move! We are calling the police.

GOLDIE: The police? Why?

BABY BEAR: Mama, that inside-out bear with no hair ate our porridge!

GOLDIE: I'm not a bear. I'm a girl!

(MAMA, PAPA, and BABY BEAR scream.)

MAMA BEAR: A girl! In our house!

PAPA BEAR: How did you get in?

GOLDIE: You're scared of me? I should be scared of you!

BABY BEAR: Make her go away, Papa!

PAPA BEAR: Police!

(OFFICER BEN, a bear, pops in.)

OFFICER BEN: Did someone say "police"?

PAPA BEAR: Yes! This . . . girl is in our house.

OFFICER BEN: Why are you in this house?

GOLDIE: I got hungry.

BABY BEAR: And she ate our porridge!

GOLDIE: Then I got tired.

BABY BEAR: So she slept in my bed!

OFFICER BEN: Let me get this straight. Little girl, you broke into this house, ate their porridge, and went to sleep in their beds?

GOLDIE: Yes.

OFFICER BEN: You are under arrest!

GOLDIE: What?!

PAPA BEAR: Take her away!

GOLDIE: Wait a minute! You can't take me to jail! I'm just a little girl. I want to talk to my parents!

OFFICER BEN: OK. Parents!

(GOLDIE'S MOM and DAD pop in.)

GOLDIE'S MOM/GOLDIE'S DAD: Yes?

OFFICER BEN: This little girl broke many laws today.

GOLDIE'S MOM: What laws?

OFFICER BEN: She broke into a house and stole food.

GOLDIE: I was hungry.

GOLDIE'S MOM: She was hungry, Officer.

OFFICER BEN: I will let you off the hook this time, little girl. But no more law-breaking!

(OFFICER BEN exits.)

MAMA BEAR: Wait, Officer! These people are still in our house!

GOLDIE'S DAD: That's it, young lady. You are not allowed to walk home by yourself anymore.

GOLDIE: Then how will I get home?

GOLDIE'S DAD: You will have to stay at school and be in the after-school program.

PAPA BEAR: I don't care where you go or what you do. You must get out of our house!

GOLDIE'S MOM: My, these bears are very upset! Maybe we should go home.

(GOLDIE, GOLDIE'S DAD, and GOLDIE'S MOM exit.)

MAMA BEAR: Those creatures were so hairless!

PAPA BEAR: We are all safe now.

BABY BEAR: Mama, will you make some more porridge?

MAMA BEAR: Of course, Baby Bear.

(EMILY and LEXIE enter.)

LEXIE/EMILY: Goldie?

(The BEARS see the GIRLS. The GIRLS see the BEARS.)

BEARS/LEXIE/EMILY: Aaaaaaaaahhhhhhhhh!!!

Questions

1. What do you think of Goldie's parents?
   What is her mom like? What is her dad like?
   What do they think about Goldie's actions?

2. Do you think Goldie should go to jail? Why or
   why not?

3. Why are the bears scared of Goldie?

4. Show the class how bears might walk.

5. Does Goldie get punished? How would you
   punish Goldie?

ENDING 2: GOLDIE THE GREAT

The bears adopt Goldie.

Characters

Baby Bear
Mama Bear
Papa Bear
Goldie

BABY BEAR: Mama, Papa, someone is sleeping in my bed!

MAMA BEAR: And someone has eaten our porridge!

PAPA BEAR: Grrrrr! Wake up, whoever you are!

(GOLDIE wakes up.)

GOLDIE: Who is talking? I'm trying to sleep!

PAPA BEAR: It's a little girl!

MAMA BEAR: She looks sweet!

GOLDIE: Are you going to eat me?

BABY BEAR: We eat porridge and honey.

GOLDIE: Oh. Are you going to yell at me?

PAPA BEAR: No, no, no. We are peaceful bears.

GOLDIE: Oh! Then what are you going to do?

MAMA BEAR: We are going to adopt you!

GOLDIE/BABY BEAR: What?

MAMA BEAR: You are going to be our little girl now!

PAPA BEAR: Baby Bear, you have a new sister!

BABY BEAR: I don't want a sister!

MAMA BEAR: Baby Bear, be nice to your new sister.

PAPA BEAR: Mama Bear, let's buy her a bike.

BABY BEAR: But I want a bike!

MAMA BEAR: You are not old enough for a bike.

GOLDIE: I already have a bike. Can I have a pony?

BABY BEAR: No fair! She's new around here, and she gets all the good stuff!

PAPA BEAR: That's enough.

BABY BEAR: But—but—but—she came into our house and ate our porridge! She should be in trouble!

GOLDIE: Mmmm—that porridge was just right!

MAMA BEAR: She was probably hungry.

GOLDIE: I was!

PAPA BEAR: Go to bed, young bear.

BABY BEAR: No fair! I hate sisters!

MAMA BEAR: Go to bed, Baby Bear.

BABY BEAR: But she's in my bed!

GOLDIE: This bed is just right!

BABY BEAR: That's my bed!

GOLDIE: Can I have that pony now?

Questions

1. Have you ever felt like Baby Bear?

2. What are some things you think are unfair?

3. Has anyone ever told you that you were too young to have something? If so, what was it?

4. Why do Mama and Papa Bear might want to adopt Goldie?

5. Would you want to have Goldie as your sister? Would you want to be Goldie's mother or father? Why or why not?

RAPUNZEL

A play with three scenes.

SCENE 1: THE PRINCE ARRIVES

The Prince arrives at the tower to save Rapunzel.

Characters
Prince
Rapunzel

PRINCE: Rapunzel, Rapunzel, let down your hair!

RAPUNZEL: Why?

PRINCE: So I can come visit you.

RAPUNZEL: I can see you from here.

PRINCE: But won't it be more fun if we're in the same room?

RAPUNZEL: I guess so, but I don't want you climbing my hair.

PRINCE: Why not?

RAPUNZEL: It will hurt!

PRINCE: It will?

RAPUNZEL: Of course it will! It's attached to my head. Couldn't you try taking the stairs?

PRINCE: But the witch locked the door!

RAPUNZEL: Break the door down!

PRINCE: It's a very big, thick door.

RAPUNZEL: Why don't you come back with a thief? The thief can pick the lock on the door.

PRINCE: Isn't that illegal?

RAPUNZEL: It's also illegal to lock a girl up in a tower.

PRINCE: Oh. OK. *(Starts to leave.)*

RAPUNZEL: Wait a minute! Bring a hairdresser, too. I want a haircut.

PRINCE: Why? You have long, beautiful hair!

RAPUNZEL: It takes me ten hours to brush it! And it weighs a ton. I want a haircut.

PRINCE: But—but—your hair is so long and beautiful!

RAPUNZEL: It's my hair. I can do whatever I want with it.

PRINCE: But—But—the fortune-teller said that I was to marry a maiden with long, beautiful hair!

RAPUNZEL: I'm too young to get married anyway.

PRINCE: Well, then, you are not my princess.

RAPUNZEL: Aren't princes supposed to rescue maidens? Isn't that your job?

PRINCE: We don't really have jobs. We just rescue maidens because we like to.

RAPUNZEL: Sounds like you only like to rescue maidens who will marry you.

PRINCE: No! Not exactly.

RAPUNZEL: I could really use some rescuing. I'm sick of this tower. You're the first person I've seen in years. It is very, very boring here.

PRINCE: Are you sure I couldn't just climb your hair?

RAPUNZEL: Oh, very well.

Questions

1. Why does the Prince want to climb Rapunzel's hair?

2. Name three things that would be bad about having long, long, long, long hair.

3. Do you think the Prince will save Rapunzel, even though she doesn't want to marry him?

SCENE 2: THE PRINCE ENTERS THE TOWER

The Prince gets in the tower—but can't get out!

Characters

Prince
Rapunzel
Witch

RAPUNZEL: That hurt a lot! You're heavy!

PRINCE: Your hair is very thick, like rope.

RAPUNZEL: But my head is very delicate!

PRINCE: I'm rescuing you! Aren't you happy?

RAPUNZEL: I'm sorry. You're right. Thank you, Prince, for rescuing me from this tower.

PRINCE: You're welcome.

(Beat.)

RAPUNZEL: So?

PRINCE: Right. I'm going to get you out of here!

RAPUNZEL: OK.

(The PRINCE looks around the room.)

PRINCE: I will try the door!

RAPUNZEL: The door is locked. Do you think I've been sitting up here for years and years and never tried opening the door?

PRINCE: Of course you tried opening the door. It's just that . . .

RAPUNZEL: You don't know what to do next, do you?

PRINCE: I just need to think a little. I will come up with a brilliant plan!

RAPUNZEL: Now we're both stuck up here. Why did you think climbing my hair would help us escape?

PRINCE: Your best idea was for me to get a thief to steal you out of here.

RAPUNZEL: That's a good idea! Why didn't you do that?

PRINCE: I'm a Prince! I can't be seen with thieves, stealing girls!

RAPUNZEL: Why, oh why, couldn't a thief be the first person to find me after years and years of being trapped in this tower?

PRINCE: How old are you anyway?

RAPUNZEL: Nine.

PRINCE: That's not so long to be trapped in a tower.

RAPUNZEL: OK, I'm eighty-seven.

PRINCE: Eighty-seven! You are too old to be my bride.

RAPUNZEL: I didn't say I would marry you!

PRINCE: Whew! That was a close call.

RAPUNZEL: You're very rude.

PRINCE: I'm rude? I think you're rude!

WITCH: *(Enters suddenly.)* I'm the rudest one of all!

RAPUNZEL/PRINCE: The witch!

Questions

1. Do you like the Prince? Why or why not?

2. Do you like Rapunzel? Why or why not?

3. How would you get Rapunzel out of the tower?

4. Who is smarter—the Prince or Rapunzel? Why?

5. Why does Rapunzel think the Prince is rude?
   Is she right or wrong?

SCENE 3: THE WITCH ARRIVES

Rapunzel learns a lot about herself!

Characters

Rapunzel
Prince
Witch

RAPUNZEL: The witch! What will we do?

PRINCE: The witch! Where will we go?

WITCH: You're trapped! Ha, ha, ha, haaaaa! Now we must all live here together, eating cookies forever and ever!

PRINCE: That rhymes!

WITCH: I know!

PRINCE: So you sit here and eat cookies all the time? What's so bad about that? I think I'm going to like being trapped here.

RAPUNZEL: Please, set me free! I long to know what broccoli tastes like.

PRINCE: You're not missing anything. It's really not that good.

RAPUNZEL: I don't care! I long to see, hear, and taste new things!

WITCH: Well, too bad, missy.

PRINCE: Excuse me, Witch, may I ask you a question?

WITCH: Certainly, Prince.

PRINCE: If she's eighty-seven, why doesn't she look old?

WITCH: She's my daughter, sonny. We witches age slowly.

PRINCE: So how old are you?

WITCH: Five billion and two.

PRINCE: Whoa!

RAPUNZEL: Wait a minute—I'm a witch?

WITCH: Yes.

RAPUNZEL: So all this time I've been able to do magic, too?

WITCH: Yep.

RAPUNZEL: Why didn't you tell me?

WITCH: You're too young to be going off on your own.

RAPUNZEL: I'm eighty-seven!

WITCH: You're just a baby.

RAPUNZEL: Door—unlock! Good-bye! I'm leaving at last!

(RAPUNZEL exits.)

PRINCE: Where are those cookies?

WITCH: They're coming; they're coming.

PRINCE: You have very long and beautiful hair.

WITCH: Why, thank you.

PRINCE: Five billion and two isn't that old.

WITCH: My mother lived to be kazillion.

PRINCE: Want to get married?

WITCH: OK.

Questions

1. If you found out you had magical powers, what would you do?

2. How do you think Rapunzel used her powers after she left the tower?

3. Can you think of any interesting way Rapunzel could use her long hair after she gets it cut off?

4. Do you think the Prince and the Witch will live happily ever after? Why or why not?

HANSEL AND GRETEL

A play with four scenes.

SCENE 1: HUNGRY

Hansel and Gretel are told to go to the woods to look for food.

Characters

Gretel
Hansel
Mother
Father

GRETEL: I'm hungry.

HANSEL: I'm hungry, too.

MOTHER: We're all hungry. There's no food.

FATHER: I'm sorry, children.

HANSEL: Why is there no food?

FATHER: I do not have a job.

GRETEL: Why not?

FATHER: There are no jobs anywhere. No one has any money.

HANSEL: What can we do?

MOTHER: We must go searching in the woods for food.

GRETEL: I don't like the woods! It's dark and scary.

MOTHER: We have no choice. We will go in pairs. I will go hunting with your father, and you children will search together for mushrooms and berries.

FATHER: You children must be very brave and have very sharp eyes. Meet us back here by nightfall.

HANSEL: How will we find our way home?

MOTHER: This is the last of our bread. Leave a trail of crumbs behind you.

HANSEL: Won't the birds in the woods eat it?

GRETEL: And the rabbits and wolves and squirrels?

MOTHER: It is all we have. Be careful.

FATHER: Remember to head back home before nightfall.

MOTHER: And stick together!

Questions

1. Why doesn't the family search for food all together? Why are the children sent out without an adult? Is this a good idea or a bad idea?

2. Why do many fairy tales take place in the woods?

3. Why do you think children are hungry in many fairy tales?

4. How is this version of Hansel and Gretel different from the one you know?

SCENE 2: IN THE WOODS

Hansel and Gretel eat some dream berries.

Characters

Hansel
Gretel
Turtle
Raccoon

HANSEL: I'll look for mushrooms. You look for berries.

GRETEL: How will we know if they're poisonous or not?

HANSEL: I don't know. Mother and Father will tell us.

GRETEL: Mother and Father sent us out into the woods alone. I don't think they love us anymore.

HANSEL: We're not alone. We're together.

GRETEL: Why couldn't I go search for food with Mother and you go search for food with Father? That would make more sense. Then we'd both be with a grown-up.

HANSEL: I guess so. But they're hunting. Father says I'm too young to hunt still.

GRETEL: Is it getting dark?

HANSEL: We just left the house! It won't be dark for hours.

GRETEL: I don't see any berries here.

HANSEL: Let's split up so we can look in more places.

GRETEL: Mother and Father said not to split up. There are wild animals in the woods.

HANSEL: You've been reading too many stories. Here. Take some of the bread. You go to the left, I'll go to the right.

GRETEL: Hansel, we should stick together.

HANSEL: Gretel, don't be a scaredy-cat.

GRETEL: If I die, it will be all your fault.

HANSEL: You won't die, silly! *(Exits to the right.)*

GRETEL: I'm so very hungry! Oh! Here are some berries. It won't hurt if I eat a few. They look so juicy and delicious! *(Eats some berries.)* Mmmm. *(Beat.)* Whoa. I feel funny. Maybe I'll just sit down for a minute.

(A TURTLE enters.)

TURTLE: Hello, little girl.

GRETEL: I'm not supposed to talk to strangers.

TURTLE: You're talking now.

GRETEL: No, I'm not.

TURTLE: Yes, you are.

GRETEL: Not anymore.

TURTLE: You didn't eat those berries, did you?

GRETEL: M—maybe I did.

TURTLE: Uh-oh. You must feel funny.

GRETEL: Why are you talking? You're a turtle.

TURTLE: See what I mean? Who knows what you'll see next!

GRETEL: What's that over there?

TURTLE: What's what?

GRETEL: That house with the candy canes.

TURTLE: Maybe you should rest.

GRETEL: Mmmm! Candy . . . *(Exits to the left.)*

HANSEL: *(Enters from the right.)* Gretel! I think it's time to go home! Gretel? Gretel? Hey, look! Gretel, you missed some berries! Right here under her nose, and she didn't even pick them. I guess I'll do it. One for the basket, one for me. One for the basket, one for me. One for the— *(Sits suddenly.)*

(A RACCOON enters.)

RACCOON: Berries—delicious! Hey, kid! Wake up!

HANSEL: I think something's wrong with those berries.

RACCOON: Yeah, they're dream berries.

HANSEL: Look! There's gingerbread house!

RACCOON: Be careful, little boy!

Questions

1. Would you have eaten those berries? Why or why not?

2. How do you feel and act when you are hungry?

3. Do you think the animals are talking to Hansel and Gretel or are they imagining it?

SCENE 3: IN THE GINGERBREAD HOUSE

The witch tries to eat Hansel and Gretel, but they have a plan!

Characters

Gretel
Hansel
Witch

HANSEL and GRETEL sit inside a house with big, big bellies. There is a big, square oven in the middle of the house.

GRETEL: I ate a lot.

HANSEL: I ate a superlot!

(The WITCH enters.)

WITCH: And now I will eat you!

GRETEL: A witch!

HANSEL: Don't you eat my sister!

WITCH: OK. I will just eat you.

GRETEL: Don't you eat my brother!

WITCH: Too bad! I will eat you both.

GRETEL: What will we do?

HANSEL: I don't know. We are doomed!

GRETEL: Maybe Mother and Father will save us!

WITCH: No one is around for miles and miles!

HANSEL: We must be clever, Gretel. Think!

WITCH: Get into my oven! I will turn it on and
make you into meatballs!

GRETEL: Oh no!

HANSEL: We will fight you, old witch.

WITCH: I am magic. You won't win.

GRETEL: I have an idea! Come here, Hansel!

*(GRETEL pulls HANSEL away from the
WITCH.)*

GRETEL: Let's get into the oven before it's hot.

HANSEL: You want to get into the oven?

GRETEL: This whole house is made of candy and
cakes! We will eat the back wall of the oven and
make our escape!

HANSEL: What a good idea!

WITCH: What are you talking about?

HANSEL/GRETEL: Nothing!

HANSEL: We want to get into the oven now.

WITCH: I knew you would see things my way. Go on. Get in.

(HANSEL and GRETEL get in the oven.)

WITCH: Let's see. How do we turn this thing on again? First I turn this knob, then I wiggle this over here . . .

(HANSEL and GRETEL appear outside the gingerbread house.)

GRETEL: Ha, ha! We are free!

HANSEL: Good-bye, old witch!

WITCH: How did you do that? Now I don't have any children to eat with my cookies. Oh, well.

Questions

1. What happens to the gingerbread house in the rain? Draw a picture of it!

2. Why would a witch live in a gingerbread house?

3. If you saw a house made of cakes and candy, would you eat it, even if it belonged to someone else?

SCENE 4: BACK AT HOME

Hansel and Gretel come home with very full bellies!

Characters

Mother
Father
Hansel
Gretel

MOTHER and FATHER sit nervously waiting.

MOTHER: Father, where could the children be?

FATHER: Don't worry, Mother. They will find their way home.

MOTHER: What if they got lost?

FATHER: Let's get some candles and go look for them.

(HANSEL and GRETEL enter suddenly. They still have big bellies.)

HANSEL: Mother!

GRETEL: Father!

HANSEL/GRETEL: We're home!

MOTHER: Oh, children, we are so happy to see you!

FATHER: We were so worried!

MOTHER: Are you OK?

HANSEL: We are OK. We saw this witch in a gingerbread house—

GRETEL: —and she wanted to eat us, but we ate the back of the oven—

HANSEL/GRETEL: —and we got away!

MOTHER: Oh, good!

FATHER: Are you sure there was a witch?

HANSEL: Yes, yes!

GRETEL: We saw her!

FATHER: I see dream-berry juice on your fingers.

HANSEL: We ate some berries, too. Oh no!

MOTHER: What?

HANSEL: We forgot to bring the berries home!

FATHER: That's all right. You see, while we were in the woods, we met a woodcutter. He gave me a new job.

GRETEL: So we will have food again?

FATHER: Yes!

MOTHER: But look at you, children. Your bellies have grown big and round.

FATHER: I think they ate too many dream berries.

GRETEL: Berries won't make your belly big.

HANSEL: It was the witch's house! It was made of candy and cakes.

FATHER: Dream berries make your bellies extra big.

MOTHER: Well, there's only one thing you can do now.

HANSEL/GRETEL: What?

MOTHER: Exercise!

HANSEL/GRETEL: Do we have to?

FATHER: We are all going to live happily ever after.

(The WITCH pops in.)

WITCH: Except me! I never get any meatballs! I need protein!

Questions

1. What is protein and why does the witch want it?

2. What makes up a healthy meal?

3. If you had to exercise and exercise and exercise, would it still be worth eating a house made of candy and cake? Why or why not?

4. Should Hansel and Gretel be mad at their mother and father for sending them out into the woods by themselves?

5. Do you think the adventure with the witch really happened?

Part 3
BRAND-NEW TALES

What is this character saying?
Where is she?
You decide!

CAVEMAN NEEDS A SHAVE, MAN

Two children run across a caveman!

Characters

Ava
Ron
Urp

AVA: Where are we?

RON: I don't know.

AVA: Shh! Did you hear that?

RON: No.

AVA: It sure is dark in here.

RON: Ouch!

AVA: Sorry!

RON: Do you think we are the first people to come to this cave?

AVA: We are probably not the first people to come here.

RON: Do you think someone is here now?

AVA: Don't scare me, Ron!

RON: Shh! Did you hear that?

AVA: No.

(Suddenly, URP jumps out.)

URP: Ooga-booga!

(RON and AVA yell!)

URP: Oogitee-boogitee!

AVA: Let's get outta here!

RON: He's a caveman!

AVA: I know!

RON: We'll be famous!

AVA: What? Let's go!

RON: No way! Let's bring him home!

URP: Grubba-grubba.

AVA: What is he saying?

RON: Grubba-grubba.

AVA: I heard him, but what does it mean?

RON: How should I know? Do I look like I speak caveman?

URP: Bleh-bleh dorf!

RON: I saw a movie where some guys found a caveman. The caveman was really cool.

AVA: I saw a real caveman, and he was scary!

RON: You mean him?

AVA: Yes! Let's go, Ron!

RON: Do you wanna come home with us?

URP: Uga-uga!

RON: See, he wants to come home with us!

AVA: Maybe he said he wants to kill us.

RON: Why would he want to kill us, Ava?

AVA: Maybe he's hungry.

RON: He won't eat us. He's human, too.

> (URP *starts jumping up and down and yelling.*
> AVA *starts yelling, too. Then* RON *starts yelling*
> *and jumping up and down, too, just for fun.)*

RON: This is awesome!

AVA: I'm getting out of here.

URP: Wait a minute. Do you know the way to
town?

AVA: You can talk!

RON: I told you he was cool!

URP: Well, I am really just a regular old human. I
got sick of cars and cell phones and people, so I
moved out here to this cave.

AVA: Why did you scare us like that?

RON: I wasn't scared!

URP: I'm sorry. I like my privacy! I couldn't help myself.

AVA: Then why do you want to go to town?

URP: I want to go to the swimming pool. I haven't had a bath in years.

RON: Awesome!

AVA: Yuck! You shouldn't take a bath in a swimming pool!

URP: Why not?

AVA: It's yucky!

URP: This is why I don't like people. Out here in my cave, there are no rules.

RON: See you later, Ava. I'm moving in with this guy here!

AVA: I'm telling Mom and Dad!

(AVA exits.)

URP: Welcome to the cave, kid!

Questions

1. Would you explore the cave?

2. Would you run away after discovering the caveman?

3. Why does Ron want to bring the caveman home? Would you want to bring a caveman home?

4. How do you think a caveman might act in a modern home?

5. Why does Urp want to live in a cave?

6. Why does he pretend to be a caveman?

7. What do you think is fun or hard about being a cave person?

8. When did cavemen and cavewomen exist?

9. How are cave people different from us today?

10. Which do you like better—being in the country or being in the city? Why?

11. What is good about being in nature?

12. What is not so good about being in nature?

THE BEAST OF
APPLETREE STREET

Julie discovers a terrible surprise.

Characters

Julie
Alex
Amanda
Fran
PJ
Connor

ALEX, FRAN, PJ, and AMANDA are standing around. JULIE enters, but we only see her from the back.

JULIE: Hi, guys!

ALEX: Aaaaaaahhhhhh!

JULIE: Amanda, what's wrong?

AMANDA: You—you—you—

JULIE: What about me?

FRAN: You're—

PJ: —a monster!

JULIE: What? Very funny.

ALEX: No, really!

JULIE: It's not funny!

AMANDA: W-w-w-we are not b-b-b-being f-f-f-f-funny!

(JULIE turns around. She has a fuzzy face.)

JULIE: *(Looking down at herself.)* I look fine. Just like always!

FRAN: You're—

PJ: —fuzzy!

FRAN: Your—

PJ/FRAN: —face!

JULIE: My face is . . . *(JULIE touches her face.)* Aaaaaaaaahhhhhhhhhh!!! I'm a beast!

AMANDA: It isn't that b-b-b-bad.

JULIE: You're scared of me!

ALEX: I'm not.

PJ: You screamed.

ALEX: I was surprised.

FRAN: You kind of look like my dog.

JULIE: I want to look like a girl, not a dog!

(CONNOR enters, laughing.)

CONNOR: I got you!

JULIE: What?

CONNOR: I got you.

JULIE: You did this to me?

CONNOR: I glued cat hair to your face while you were sleeping.

PJ: How did you get cat hair?

CONNOR: I shaved the cat.

FRAN: That's mean!

AMANDA: I feel so much better now!

JULIE: Well, I don't! I have cat hair stuck on my face!

ALEX: My dad shaves his face. You could shave your face, too.

JULIE: You are in trouble, Connor! *(Exits.)*

PJ: I can't believe you did that.

(JULIE enters quickly.)

JULIE: Nobody tell about this at school! *(Exits again.)*

Questions

1. What do you think happens next?

2. Does Julie ever get the hair off her face?

3. Will Connor get in trouble? What should be his punishment?

4. Do you think Connor's joke is funny?

5. How would you react if Connor played that joke on you?

6. Draw a picture of Julie with the hair on her face and without the hair on her face!

THE PRESIDENT'S DOG

*Life as the president's dog is
very good, indeed.*

Characters

Bill
Lucy
Linda
Harry
Angela
Grace
Lara
Ted
Tara

BILL: Here, Lucy! Come on, girl!

(LUCY enters. She is the president's dog.)

HARRY: What a good girl. Come here, I have some
dog food for you!

*(LUCY dances around, happy. She walks over to
her food and turns up her nose.)*

LINDA: Lucy, you are so picky. This is good food!

(LUCY shakes her head.)

BILL: What do you want? Steak?

(LUCY nods her head.)

HARRY: Steak?! You sure are a spoiled dog.

LINDA: She is the president's dog.

BILL: She gets better food than anyone else in the White House.

(LUCY nods her head. ANGELA enters.)

ANGELA: Where's my dog? Oh, there you are, Lucy.

HARRY: President Angela, Lucy won't eat her food!

ANGELA: Why not?

LINDA: She wants steak!

ANGELA: Then get her steak!

BILL: Yes, President Angela!

(LUCY blows a raspberry at BILL, LINDA, and HARRY. They exit.)

ANGELA: Now, Lucy, be nice and polite! You are a president's dog.

(LUCY looks ashamed.)

ANGELA: Here come the children!

(GRACE and LARA enter.)

ANGELA: I have to go work. I will see you later.

(ANGELA exits.)

GRACE/LARA: Bye, Mom!

(LUCY *waves good-bye.*)

GRACE: Oh, Lucy, you're so cute!

(LUCY *poses and shows off for Grace.*)

LARA: Lucy, you ate my shoes!

(LUCY *rubs her belly. TED and TARA enter.*)

TED: Can I get my picture taken with—

LARA: Well, OK.

(LARA *stands next to TED and smiles.*)

TED: No, no. Not you! I want my picture taken with Lucy!

(LUCY *smiles and bats her eyelashes.*)

LARA: Fine!

(LARA *exits. TARA takes a picture of TED and LUCY.*)

TARA: My turn!

(TED *takes a picture of TARA and LUCY.*)

TED/TARA: Thank you!

(TED *and TARA exit.*)

GRACE: Lucy, I want to play with you alllll day. I love you.

(HARRY, BILL, and LINDA enter.)

HARRY: Here's your steak, Lucy!

LINDA: The chef made it just for you!

BILL: You are the luckiest dog in the world, Lucy.

   (LUCY nods.)

Questions

1. Do you think Lucy is the luckiest dog in the world? Why?

2. Do you think Lucy is spoiled?

3. What would you want to do if you were the president's dog?

4. If you were the president, what kind of dog would you want?

5. Do you like dogs?

6. How can a person act out being a dog?

7. Does Lara like Lucy?

8. Do Harry, Linda, and Bill like Lucy?

9. Would you want your picture taken with Lucy?

10. What would it be like to be famous?

11. Where is the White House?

THE BEST

Rex thinks he's the best.

Characters

Sandy
Rex
Debra
Mel

REX, SANDY, DEBRA, and MEL stand together wearing coats, hats, and gloves. It is very cold.

SANDY: My mitten has a hole in it.

REX: My gloves are new. They cost a hundred dollars.

DEBRA: No, they didn't.

REX: Yes, they did. My dad bought them in Mexico.

MEL: Mexico is hot. They don't have gloves in Mexico.

REX: Have you ever been to Mexico?

MEL: No.

REX: Then how do you know?

SANDY: I'm cold.

DEBRA: Me, too.

REX: Once I was on the top of a mountain. I got so cold that I froze into ice, and they had to melt me.

DEBRA: Melt you? That doesn't make sense. If they melted you, you'd be a puddle now.

REX: They melted the ice off of me.

SANDY: Can a person turn into ice?

MEL: No.

REX: Have you ever been on the top of a mountain?

MEL: No, and you weren't either.

REX: Yes, I was.

SANDY: Why were you there?

REX: I was skiing with my dad. My dad is the richest man in the world.

DEBRA: The richest man in the world? Maybe he's the richest man in America. But I doubt that.

REX: It's true.

MEL: If you are so rich, why do you go to school?

SANDY: Rich people have to go to school.

MEL: He lives in a regular house, just like the rest of us. If he were rich, he'd live in a huge mansion.

SANDY: That's true.

DEBRA: You're lying, Rex. Lying is bad.

REX: I am not lying! You just don't understand.

SANDY: We will still like you, Rex, even if you are not rich.

REX: You guys are stupid. You don't understand.

DEBRA: We are not stupid! You're stupid.

MEL: Maybe I am the richest boy in the world.

REX: You are not.

MEL: How do you know?

REX: Because I am!

SANDY: I'm cold.

DEBRA: Maybe Rex's dad can buy you new mittens.

MEL: Mexican mittens!

REX: I bet he could buy you new mittens. If he felt like it.

Questions

1. Is Rex lying? Is he really the richest boy in the world?

2. Why do people lie?

3. Do you think Rex's friends will like him more or less if he tells the truth?

4. Why do people sometimes pretend to have more than they really have (like toys or money)?

5. Is it better to be rich or poor?

6. Does being rich make you a better person inside?

7. What can an actor do to show he or she is cold, even when it's actually very warm?

THE FORTUNE-TELLER

Does Martin have the winning lottery ticket?

Characters

Madame Luba
Stephanie
Martin

MADAME LUBA: I will tell your future!

STEPHANIE: OK.

MADAME LUBA: Oh my!

STEPHANIE: What is it?

MADAME LUBA: Do not go to Dallas!

STEPHANIE: Why? I was about to get on an airplane and go to Dallas today!

MADAME LUBA: You will lose your luggage!

STEPHANIE: No!

MADAME LUBA: Yes!

STEPHANIE: Thank you, Madame Luba! I will not go to Dallas!

MADAME LUBA: You are a smart girl. NEXT!

(STEPHANIE exits. MARTIN enters carrying books and papers.)

MARTIN: I think I am next. But I do not believe in fortune-tellers.

MADAME LUBA: You are a silly boy! I can see the future!

MARTIN: Then where am I going next?

MADAME LUBA: The library!

MARTIN: How did you guess?

MADAME LUBA: You are holding a library card!

MARTIN: Oh. I am. Tell me something else about my future.

MADAME LUBA: You have a lottery ticket!

MARTIN: Yes, I am also holding that in my hand.

MADAME LUBA: You will . . . you will—WIN!

MARTIN: I will?

MADAME LUBA: No, you will lose. Give me the lottery ticket, and I will throw it away. It is garbage.

MARTIN: OK—Wait! I think you are lying to me.

MADAME LUBA: No!

MARTIN: Maybe you want my lottery ticket for yourself!

MADAME LUBA: Nah.

MARTIN: Then I will throw it away outside.

MADAME LUBA: Nooo!

MARTIN: A-ha! I was right! This is the winning lottery ticket!

MADAME LUBA: I thought you did not believe in fortune-tellers.

MARTIN: I don't.

MADAME LUBA: Then give me that ticket.

MARTIN: I don't wanna.

MADAME LUBA: Give it to me!

MARTIN: No!

MADAME LUBA: OK. Then I won't tell you what else I see.

MARTIN: Tell me, please!

MADAME LUBA: I don't wanna.

MARTIN: Madame Luba, I beg you!

MADAME LUBA: Nah.

MARTIN: What is in my future? I must know!

MADAME LUBA: You must know?

MARTIN: Yes!

MADAME LUBA: Then give me that lottery ticket!

MARTIN: Ooooooooh, very well!

(MARTIN hands a slip of paper to MADAME LUBA.)

MARTIN: Now what else is in my future?

MADAME LUBA: You will buy flip-flops in the summer.

MARTIN: And?

MADAME LUBA: That's it.

MARTIN: That's it?!

MADAME LUBA: Yes.

MARTIN: You have some nerve!

(MARTIN exits.)

MADAME LUBA: Ha, ha, ha! *(Looks at the slip of paper.)* Wait a minute—this is a coupon for fifty cents off granola bars. *(Yelling.)* YOU HAVE SOME NERVE, BUDDY!

Questions

1. Is it fair for Martin to trick the fortune-teller? Did he do it on purpose or by accident?

2. Is it fair for Madame Luba to trick Martin?

3. Do you think Martin will win the lottery?

4. Can Madame Luba see the future?

5. Would you want to be able to see the future?

6. What do you think Madame Luba's voice sounds like? How does she move?

7. How does Martin walk and talk?

8. Do you think Stephanie should go to Dallas even if she will lose her luggage?

9. Where is Dallas?

MY KINGDOM

Alexander wants to take over the kingdom from his sister, Mary.

Characters

Mary
Alexander
Lizabeth
Luke
Jane

MARY sits on a throne. ALEXANDER stands in front of her.

MARY: Bow before me!

ALEXANDER: Never!

MARY: How dare you!

ALEXANDER: I am the King. You should not be sitting on that throne!

MARY: Be quiet and obey me. I am your Queen.

(LIZABETH enters.)

LIZABETH: Be quiet, both of you! The servants can hear you.

MARY: I am the Queen. I don't care what the servants think.

ALEXANDER: The people of this land love me. They know I am the true ruler of this kingdom.

MARY: Stop complaining, Alexander! Father gave me this kingdom because he knows that you are not fit to rule.

ALEXANDER: Yes, I am!

MARY: I am older than you, and you can't even keep your room clean.

ALEXANDER: So what?

MARY: And I heard you say that you were sorry to the maid yesterday for getting in her way!

ALEXANDER: So?

MARY: So a king must tell people what to do! A king should never apologize!

ALEXANDER: Why not?

MARY: Because a king or a queen is always right.

ALEXANDER: That is your problem, Mary. You think you know everything!

MARY: I do know everything.

ALEXANDER: No, you don't.

MARY: Yes, I do!

ALEXANDER: No, you don't!

MARY: I'm going to chop your head off!

ALEXANDER: No, you won't!

MARY: Yes, I will!

ALEXANDER: No, you—

LIZABETH: Enough! That's it. I'm taking over. All you two do is argue all day and night. Mary, you are bossy and unkind. Alexander, you are whiny, and you can't make any decisions. I am the Queen now.

ALEXANDER: Don't be silly!

MARY: Off with her head! Servants!

(LUKE and JANE enter.)

LUKE: Yes, my Queen?

MARY: Please chop Lizabeth's and Alexander's heads off.

LUKE: Um, I don't think I want to.

MARY: What?! How dare you! Jane, chop off their heads.

JANE: Pardon me, Queen, but that would make a terrible mess.

MARY: So what?

JANE: I am the maid, and I would have to clean up the mess.

ALEXANDER: See? All of your subjects have turned against you!

MARY: Nonsense. Luke, who do you like best— Alexander, Lizabeth, or me? Keep in mind that I might chop your head off if you give me the wrong answer.

LUKE: Ummmmm, I like Lizabeth the best.

ALEXANDER: Lizabeth?!

MARY: Why?

LUKE: She isn't sloppy or bossy.

MARY: I am not sloppy!

ALEXANDER: I am not bossy! Who do you like best, Jane?

JANE: Lizabeth.

ALEXANDER: This is shocking!

MARY: Disgusting! Servants! Off with their heads!

LUKE: Ma'am?

MARY: Yes?

JANE: We are the only servants.

LUKE: We won't chop each other's heads off.

MARY: Oh. Right.

LIZABETH: Well, I guess I am the Queen now. Give me the crown. Alexander, go to your room.

ALEXANDER: Aw, rats!

(ALEXANDER exits.)

LIZABETH: Mary, go to your room and think about how you've behaved.

(MARY stamps her foot and starts to leave.)

LIZABETH: Wait a minute! You are forgetting something.

MARY: What?

LIZABETH: The crown.

MARY: This is not fair!

(MARY hands her crown over to LIZABETH and exits angrily.)

LIZABETH: Luke? Jane?

LUKE/JANE: Yes, Queen?

LIZABETH: Let us party.

LUKE/JANE: Yes, Queen!

Questions

1. If you were queen or king, what would you do all day?

2. You are a king or queen. Write the laws of your land.

3. Which person—Lizabeth, Mary, or Alexander—makes the best ruler? Why?

4. Do you think Mary means it when she says, "Off with her head!"

5. How would you treat your subjects if you were the king or the queen?

6. How do kings and queens sit? Stand? Walk? How is it different from you sit, stand, and walk?

7. Do kings and queens speak differently? See if you can say Mary, Alexander, or Lizabeth's lines like a king or queen.

8. How is a castle different from a regular house or apartment? Can you picture a big room in a castle? Do you act differently in a castle than you do in an everyday place?

BRRRR!

*Martha and Bob get lost and
end up in an igloo.*

Characters

Uma
Lakshi
Bob
Martha

*Lights come up on a white space. UMA and
LAKSHMI relax on the floor. BOB and
MARTHA enter in a hurry.*

MARTHA: At last! People! Shelter! Thank God!

BOB: Man, it sure is cold out there! There's a
blizzard going on!

*(BOB and MARTHA begin to take off their
coats.)*

MARTHA/BOB: Wooo! Wow! Brrr! It's so cold!

LAKSHMI: Excuse me. Who are you?

BOB: Oh, gosh, I'm so sorry! I'm Bob and this is
Martha.

LAKSHMI: Why are you here?

MARTHA: It's freezing out there! Our car broke down, and this is the first shelter we saw!

UMA: This is our house.

MARTHA: It's lovely. I love, um, . . . *(Looking around.)* how white it is.

UMA: It's an igloo.

BOB: So—Wait a minute here. This house is made of ice?

LAKSHMI: That's right.

(BOB and MARTHA put their coats back on.)

BOB: Why would you live in a house made of ice?

UMA: We're Eskimos. That's what we do.

MARTHA: But why? It's freezing! Don't you want to be warm?

UMA: We are warm. And it keeps our fish fresh.

MARTHA: It's like living in a refrigerator!

UMA: What's a refrigerator?

LAKSHMI: Why are you in our house? It's not very nice to barge into someone's house.

BOB: It's snowing!

LAKSHMI: Uh-huh.

MARTHA: And it's twenty degrees below zero!

LAKSHMI: Uh-huh. *(Pause.)* So?

BOB: We could have died out there!

UMA: You could have at least knocked.

LAKSHMI: Or asked if you could come in.

UMA: That would be polite.

MARTHA: Are you telling us we have to leave?

LAKSHMI: I don't know . . .

BOB: If you send us away, we'll die out there!

UMA: I don't think you'll die.

MARTHA: Oh, please, let us stay!

(UMA and LAKSHMI look at each other and sigh. They look back at MARTHA and BOB.)

LAKSHMI: Well . . . OK.

UMA: I guess you can stay a little while.

LAKSHMI: But you sure were rude.

(Beat.)

MARTHA: So . . . Thank you for letting us stay. Do you have a car? If you do, then maybe you could drive us to an airport and we will get out of your way.

LAKSHMI: We don't have a car.

BOB: You don't have a car!

MARTHA: And you live in an igloo made of ice.

LAKSHMI: Right.

BOB: So what do you do all day?

LAKSHMI: We hunt and fish.

UMA: We talk to each other.

LAKSHMI: Uma likes to draw.

MARTHA: Oh! Why don't you put some of your drawings on the wall?

UMA: It's made of ice. The paper gets wet.

MARTHA: Oh. Where do you sleep?

LAKSHMI: We have some blankets.

BOB: That's it?

UMA: Are you still cold?

MARTHA/BOB: Yes!

UMA: I think it's cozy and warm.

LAKSHMI: Me, too.

UMA: Would you like to sit down?

MARTHA: That's very nice.

BOB: Don't mind if I do!

(BOB and MARTHA sit on the floor. MARTHA stands up again right away. BOB starts making terrible faces like his bottom is getting frozen.)

MARTHA: Oh!

LAKSHMI: What is it?

UMA: Is something wrong?

MARTHA: Oh . . . uh . . . I just remembered that . . . I forgot to turn off the oven at home.

UMA: What's an oven?

MARTHA: Well . . . the truth is . . . it's very cold sitting down on the ice.

LAKSHMI: *(To BOB.)* Are you cold?

BOB: Um . . . *(In pain.)* No! I'm . . . fine and dandy.

(There is a pause. BOB is in pain. MARTHA is cold and nervous. UMA and LAKSHMI are relaxed.)

MARTHA: Do you think it will stop snowing soon?

UMA: No.

LAKSHMI: Why did you come here?

BOB: We got a little bit . . . lost.

MARTHA: Bob wouldn't stop to ask for directions. I told you this isn't the way to Florida!

BOB: It looked right! Until . . . the snow.

MARTHA: Bob, you never listen to me!

BOB: Martha, stop nagging me!

MARTHA: You got us lost!

BOB: Everything is fine, Martha!

MARTHA: How is this fine! We are in an igloo in the middle of nowhere, freezing to death, with no way home! How is that fine!

BOB: Calm down, Martha!

MARTHA: Bob, we have no way to get home! We're stuck here forever!

BOB: I think we'll be very happy here!

LAKSHMI: I have a dogsled.

MARTHA/BOB: What?

LAKSHMI: I have a dogsled. I can take you into town.

UMA: You can stay in a hotel. When the weather gets better, you can take a plane to Florida.

BOB: That's wonderful!

MARTHA: It's a miracle!

LAKSHMI: Go outside. I just need to put on my coat.

BOB/MARTHA: OK!

(BOB and MARTHA exit.)

UMA: I'm so glad we live here.

LAKSHMI: Yeah. People from the South are crazy.

Questions

1. What do you think about Bob and Martha? Do you like them? Are they smart? Are they nice people?

2. What do you think about Uma and Lakshmi? Do you like them? Are they smart? Are they nice people?

3. Would you like to live in an igloo? Why or why not?

4. Can you imagine what it would be like to live with Uma and Lakshmi? Can you imagine not knowing what a refrigerator or an oven was? Can you imagine not having a TV? Hunting and fishing for your food?

5. How can you act like you're cold, even when you're not?

6. If you were Martha or Bob, what would you think about Uma and Lakshmi?

7. If you were Uma or Lakshmi, what would you think about Bob and Martha?

8. Was it right for Bob and Martha to come into Uma and Lakshmi's house?

9. Would you kick Bob and Martha out if they came to your igloo?

10. Do you think Uma and Lakshmi's life is strange or interesting?

11. How do you behave when you meet someone who lives differently than you do? Would you like to meet more people who are different from you?

THE FACTORY

A play with two scenes.

SCENE 1: THE INHERITANCE

Olivia and Tim are orphans, but they just inherited an ice cream factory!

Characters

Olivia
Tim
Mr. Leggitt
Shirley

The stage is dark. Lights slowly come on.
MR. LEGGITT enters.

MR. LEGGITT: Olivia and Tim, I know you never met anyone in your family. But we recently discovered that you are related to the great Applebaum family. Do you know who the Applebaums are?

OLIVIA: No, sir.

TIM: Who are the Applebaums?

MR. LEGGITT: They are, or were, the makers of the world-famous Applebaum Ice Cream.

TIM: Ice cream?

MR. LEGGITT: That's right. Recently, the last member of the Applebaum family, Arthur Applebaum died.

OLIVIA: Oh, that's so sad.

MR. LEGGITT: Not really. He was one hundred and eighty years old. He was tired of ice cream.

TIM: How can anyone get tired of ice cream?

OLIVIA: Be quiet, Tim!

TIM: Don't tell me what to do, Olivia!

MR. LEGGITT: Olivia and Tim, you are the last Applebaums on earth. Do you realize what this means?

TIM: We're still orphans.

OLIVIA: We have no family.

MR. LEGGITT: But you do have . . . an ice cream factory!

TIM: What?

MR. LEGGITT: Don't you see where we are? We're in an ice cream factory! And all this is yours. Olivia and Tim, you are rich!

OLIVIA: We are?

TIM: Do we have a lot of ice cream, too?

MR. LEGGITT: This is the best ice cream in the world. If you can keep this factory running, you will have all the money you want, and you can eat ice cream for breakfast, lunch, and dinner.

TIM: What will we eat for dessert?

MR. LEGGITT: More ice cream, of course!

OLIVIA: You can't eat ice cream for breakfast, lunch, dinner, and dessert, Tim. You'll get sick.

TIM: No, I won't.

OLIVIA: Besides, you'll get sick of it.

TIM: No, I won't.

OLIVIA: Mr. Leggitt, we're just children. How can we run a factory?

MR. LEGGITT: It's very easy, actually. You only have one employee, Shirley. Shirley knows everything about making ice cream. *(Calling out.)* Oh, Shirley! Shirley! Come out and meet your new bosses!

(SHIRLEY enters. She is wearing a bathrobe and slippers and is very old.)

SHIRLEY: Someone call me?

MR. LEGGITT: I did, Shirley.

SHIRLEY: Who are you?

MR. LEGGITT: I'm Mr. Leggitt.

SHIRLEY: Oh. Who is Mr. Leggitt?

MR. LEGGITT: I am.

SHIRLEY: Who are you?

MR. LEGGITT: Mr. Leggitt.

SHIRLEY: Who's Mr. Leggitt?

MR. LEGGITT: I am.

OLIVIA: Excuse me, Shirley, but Arthur Applebaum died.

SHIRLEY: Arthur Applebaum died? That's sad. He was just a young man.

OLIVIA: He was a hundred and eighty!

TIM: How old are you?

SHIRLEY: Twenty-two.

TIM: No, you're—

OLIVIA: Tim, be polite! Shirley, you know how to make the ice cream?

SHIRLEY: Of course I do! I've been doing this for a hundred years.

TIM: I thought you were twenty-two years old.

SHIRLEY: I am!

MR. LEGGITT: Olivia and Tim, I'll leave you alone now with your new factory and your employee.

(MR. LEGGITT exits.)

OLIVIA: Shirley, Tim and I own the factory now. Can you help us make ice cream?

SHIRLEY: Sure as my name's Shirley.

TIM: What kinds can you make?

SHIRLEY: All kinds.

TIM: Rocky Road?

SHIRLEY: Yes.

TIM: Tutti-Fruiti?

SHIRLEY: Yes.

TIM: Peanut-Butter Brickle?

SHIRLEY: I said all kinds.

TIM: Whoooooooa.

OLIVIA: And you make the ice cream all by yourself?

SHIRLEY: Sure do.

OLIVIA: All of the ice cream? All by yourself?

TIM: Even Beet-Root Mint-Chip Surprise?

SHIRLEY: Am I speaking English? All the kinds! All by myself!

OLIVIA: Can you show us how?

TIM: Can we make Blueberry Pumpkin Fudge?

SHIRLEY: Yes and yes. Come on over to the machine.

(SHIRLEY walks very slooooooooooooowly over to the machine. OLIVIA and TIM follow her.)

OLIVIA: Are you sure you can do this, Shirley?

SHIRLEY: I've been doing it for a hundred and ninety years! I think I've got it.

TIM: A hundred and ninety!

OLIVIA: Shhh! OK, Shirley, show us how.

(SHIRLEY takes some deep breaths. She rubs her sore back. She coughs and moans and groans.)

OLIVIA: Are you OK, Shirley?

SHIRLEY: Do I look like anything is wrong with me?

TIM: Yes.

SHIRLEY: Well, I'm fine. Here we go! *(Pressing some buttons.)* Blueberry. Pumpkin. Fudge. OK. Go! *(She presses one last button.)* There. All done.

OLIVIA: That's it? Now we're rich?

TIM: And we have all the ice cream we want?

SHIRLEY: I quit.

OLIVIA/TIM: What?!?!

SHIRLEY: I quit. You ask too many questions.

OLIVIA/TIM: Shirley, NO!

Questions

1. What do you think happens after this scene ends? Do Olivia and Tim live happily ever after? Does Shirley stay at the factory? Do Olivia and Tim learn to work the machine?

2. If Olivia and Tim get rich, what do you think they will do with the money?

3. Do you think Tim will eat only ice cream from now on? If you had an ice cream factory, would you only eat ice cream?

4. If you could live anywhere or have anything, where would you live and what would you have?

5. Mr. Leggitt is an adult, and Olivia and Tim are children. If you were acting out Mr. Leggitt, what would you do to seem older?

6. Shirley is very, very old. How would you act out Shirley? How does she talk? How does she walk? How does she cough? How does she move?

7. Would you want to live to be a hundred and eighty? Why or why not?

8. If you could create one ice cream flavor, what would it be?

9. What is an inheritance?

SCENE 2: NO SHIRLEY

The orphans can't work the ice cream machine—what next?

Characters

Tim

Olivia

TIM: I've been trying for months and months. I just can't get the ice cream machine to work! All I can do is make a lot of ice.

OLIVIA: I've been trying for months and months to find someone who knows how to use the Ice-O-Matic. This machine is so old, no one alive knows how to use it!

TIM: Except Shirley. And she's never coming back.

OLIVIA: Now what are we going to do?

TIM: All we have is a huge, empty factory filled with ice, sugar, and milk.

OLIVIA: Too bad we ate all the other ingredients.

TIM: We had to eat, Olivia.

(OLIVIA and TIM sigh.)

OLIVIA: Maybe we can sell the factory.

TIM: Or maybe we can make something else here.

OLIVIA: Like what?

TIM: I don't know.

   (OLIVIA and TIM think.)

OLIVIA: I know!

TIM: What?

OLIVIA: You said you can only get the Ice-O-Matic to make ice?

TIM: Yep, no ice cream.

OLIVIA: What if we opened an ice rink?

TIM: That's a good idea. But it will take us a while to make money. What will we eat?

OLIVIA: Maybe we have to go back to the orphanage after all.

TIM: No, I've got it!

OLIVIA: Tell me!

TIM: We could make everyone pay us a dollar to get in, plus ten Cheerios!

OLIVIA: So we could eat Cheerios? But Cheerios aren't good without milk.

TIM: Don't you remember? We have milk and sugar! We may not be able to eat ice cream all day, but we can have breakfast all day!

OLIVIA: That's perfect! I'll make some signs to tell people about the ice rink!

TIM: Remember, to get in, you have to pay one dollar and ten Cheerios.

OLIVIA: OK. You make the ice!

TIM: You got it!

OLIVIA: I think we may have a happy ending after all!

Questions

1. Do you think Tim and Olivia's plan will work?

2. Would you go to that ice rink?

3. If fifty-seven people went to the ice rink, how much money would Tim and Olivia make?

4. If four people came to the ice rink, how many Cheerios would Tim and Olivia have?

   10 + 10 + 10 + 10 = _____

5. What would you do with a factory, ice, milk, and sugar?

6. What should Tim and Olivia buy with their dollars?

Part 4

ADVANCED ADVENTURES

What are these characters saying?
Where are they?
You decide!

HUNGRY DRAGON

*Dragula is ready for his first meal in
a hundred years.*

Characters

Dragula
Norbert

DRAGULA, a dragon, rubs his eyes and stretches.

DRAGULA: Wow! It's the year 300 already? Every
hundred years I come out of my cave, get a little
fresh air, and eat the first villager I see to keep
my energy up.

*(NORBERT happily walks by with a basket of
food.)*

DRAGULA: And the first villager I see is you! Hey,
skinny little kid, it's not your lucky day. Stop
where you are so I can eat you.

NORBERT: Look, I was just walking by. I thought
you would still be in your cave. I don't want any
trouble, OK?

DRAGULA: No! Not OK! Get in my belly,
skinny boy!

NORBERT: That's right—I'm skinny! Too skinny

for you. There's not even enough of me to fill a tooth.

DRAGULA: You have food with you; why don't you eat it and get a little fatter for me?

NORBERT: My mom sent me to the market to get these tomatoes and spinach and corn and beans. I need to bring them home.

DRAGULA: Then you shouldn't have stopped by my cave.

NORBERT: I didn't think you'd be awake yet.

DRAGULA: Well, tough luck, buddy. I'm awake, and you're here. You're better than nothing!

NORBERT: Why don't I just go home and wash my feet first so I taste better.

DRAGULA: Don't try to outsmart me, kid. I haven't had a bite in one hundred years, so I'm tired of waiting. I'll just toast you lightly with my fiery breath and chew you up with my big, slimy, green teeth that I haven't brushed in ninety-nine years and three hundred and sixty-four days.

NORBERT: You haven't eaten since the year 199? That's amazing and not good for your disposition.

DRAGULA: Great! I wait a hundred years to eat somebody, and I get to eat a stupid kid! Three hundred minus one hundred equals two hundred. So you see, kid, I haven't eaten since the year 200. Two hundred plus one hundred equals three hundred, and today is New Year's Day in the year 300. Now at least you won't die stupid, kid.

NORBERT: A-ha! I think you are the one who needs some work in the math department, Mr. Rottenbreath. It's still the year 299; it won't be New Year's Day for four more days. You are not due for a meal for ninety-six hours, so I'll just be on my way now.

DRAGULA: Oh, so you mean I woke up early? Yikes, that leap year thing every four Februarys threw me off, I guess.

NORBERT: See ya, wouldn't want to be ya.

DRAGULA: Not so fast, squirt. Gimme what's in that grocery basket. I could graze on those tomatoes and beans and that corn and spinach stuff until Thursday.

NORBERT: I don't know how I'll explain this to my mom, but go ahead and eat up.

DRAGULA: Wow! This stuff is crunchier than a little boy and juicier than a puppy! It's better than anybody I've ever devoured. No hair or belly buttons to spit out, either!

(DRAGULA *makes gobbling noises, then burps.*)

NORBERT: Listen, Mr. Rottenbreath—

DRAGULA: Just call me Draggy, my little friend.

NORBERT: See, a little bit of nutrition has already improved your disposition!

DRAGULA: Aw, shucks—that rhymes! I like you enough to be your friend, but I don't like you enough to eat you anymore . . . No offense.

NORBERT: No offense taken. Go brush your big, green teeth and shine your scales, Draggy. You're invited to my house in four days for New Year's dinner. We're vegetarians. You'll love it!

DRAGGY: Can I bring my wife and kids?

NORBERT: Sure. The more the scarier.

Questions

1. Can you do the math Draggy did?

    $300 - 100 =$ _____

    $200 + 100 =$ _____

2. Do you know what leap year is? How many days
    are usually in February? How many days are in
    February during leap years?

3. Why hasn't Draggy brushed his teeth in ninety-
    nine years and three hundred and sixty-four
    days? How many days are in a year?

4. Do you think Dragula is smart? Why or
    why not?

5. What does the word negotiate mean? How does
    Norbert try to negotiate with Draggy?

6. What does it mean to be open-minded? Who is
    open-minded in this story?

7. How does Norbert show he is forgiving?

SANTA'S LITTLE HELPERS

A Pick-an-Adventure Play.

THE BEGINNING: AT THE NORTH POLE

Lottie and Ralph find Santa's workshop.

Characters

Ralph
Lottie
Jangle

RALPH: Whoa! Look where we are, Lottie!

LOTTIE: Is this . . .

RALPH/LOTTIE: It's Santa's house!

LOTTIE: Let's go!

(JANGLE stops them.)

JANGLE: Stop right there.

RALPH: Why?

JANGLE: The only people allowed in here are elves. And Santa. And Mrs. Claus. Everyone else must STAY OUT!

LOTTIE: But we're elves!

JANGLE: I've never seen you before.

RALPH: We're from down south.

JANGLE: An elf? In the south?

LOTTIE: We are tree elves. We come from the forest of . . . Keebler. We make cookies.

JANGLE: Hmmm . . . I've heard of you. Why are you here now?

RALPH: Our cookie machine—

LOTTIE: The tree oven—

RALPH: —broke down, and we need some work.

JANGLE: Work? Well, you came to the right place. It is November 25th, and there's only a month until Christmas!

LOTTIE: Great! Can we come in then?

JANGLE: Right this way!

Questions

1. How do you think Lottie and Ralph end up at the North Pole?

2. Why do you think they are there?

3. Would you offer to work for Santa? Why or why not?

Pick an Adventure!

What happens next? You decide on the ending! Choose which scene ends the story.

Ending 1: Ralph and Lottie create a new toy. For this ending, go to page 148.

Ending 2: Ralph and Lottie discover that toy making is hard work! For this ending, go to page 153.

Ending 3: Ralph and Lottie get too big to fit into the toy shop. For this ending, go to page 157.

Ending 4: Lottie steals a toy! For this ending, go to page 161.

Want another ending? Draw or write it here!

ENDING 1: THE BIGGEST TOY ON EARTH

Lottie and Ralph create the world's biggest toy.

Characters

> Jangle
> Ralph
> Lottie
> Ring-a-Ding
> Ding-a-Ling

JANGLE: Tree elves! You need to work faster!

RALPH: My fingers hurt!

LOTTIE: *(To RALPH.)* Shh! *(To JANGLE.)* Yes, Mr. Jangle.

> *(JANGLE exits.)*

RALPH: Why did you tell me to be quiet?

LOTTIE: We can't let the elves know that we are children!

RALPH: Why do you have to be an elf to work here? We are the same size as elves.

LOTTIE: Don't you see? Elves have quicker fingers that we do. They are better workers.

(RING-A-DING, another elf, enters.)

RING-A-DING: No talking!

LOTTIE: But we were talking about our work!

RING-A-DING: No talking!

RALPH: Ring-a-Ding, can we see Santa?

RING-A-DING: See Santa?

RALPH: Yes, we want to show him something.

LOTTIE: Shh!

RALPH: You shh, Lottie!

(JANGLE enters with DING-A-LING.)

JANGLE: What is going on here?

RING-A-DING: These tree elves have asked to see Santa.

JANGLE: Santa?

DING-A-LING: Santa?

RALPH: Santa!

DING-A-LING: But no one sees Santa until Christmas!

JANGLE: Elves do not ask to see Santa!

LOTTIE: Sorry! Forget we asked.

RALPH: No, I want to see Santa!

LOTTIE: But why?

RALPH: We—

LOTTIE: Shh!

RALPH: —made the world's biggest toy!

DING-A-LING: Really? Wow.

RING-A-DING: Why?

RALPH: It's amazing! It can do everything—make pancakes, do your homework, play catch with you—

LOTTIE: —make dolls and doll houses—

JANGLE: This is silly! Why would anyone want one toy to do all of those things?

RING-A-DING: Besides, the world's biggest toy won't fit into Santa's sleigh.

DING-A-LING: Your toy can really do all those things?

RALPH/LOTTIE: Yes!

DING-A-LING: Wow.

RING-A-DING: I think we should tell Santa.

JANGLE: I think we should tell Santa that these elves are disobeying orders! You are supposed to build toys, not create toys!

RALPH: Mr. Jangle, I think you are jealous!

(RING-A-DING, DING-A-LING, and LOTTIE gasp!)

JANGLE: I am not.

RALPH: You are, too.

JANGLE: I am not!

RING-A-DING: You might be.

JANGLE: How dare you!

LOTTIE: If Santa is magic, then maybe he can make our toy fit on the sleigh.

DING-A-LING: We could ask him.

RING-A-DING: Ding-a-Ling has a good point.

DING-A-LING: I do?

JANGLE: Fine! I will ask him. And you will be fired, tree elves!

(JANGLE exits. Everyone waits. After a few seconds, JANGLE re-enters.)

LOTTIE: Well?

RALPH: What did Santa say?

JANGLE: He said . . . no.

RING-A-DING: He said no?

JANGLE: No, he said yes.

DING-A-LING: But you said no.

JANGLE: I was lying! I didn't want to tell you the good news. Maybe I am jealous.

RALPH/LOTTIE: Hooray!

LOTTIE: This will be the best Christmas ever!

Questions

1. Would you want Lottie and Ralph's toy?

2. Would it be wrong to have a toy that did your homework for you?

3. If you could create any toy, what would it be?

4. Do you think Jangle was jealous of Ralph and Lottie? Why?

5. Which elf do you like best? Why?

6. Do you think Ralph and Lottie's toy will fit in Santa's sleigh?

7. Do you think Ralph and Lottie should be fired for creating toys instead of just building them?

ENDING 2: ESCAPE FROM THE NORTH POLE

Lottie and Ralph decide they do not like working as elves!

Characters

Lottie
Ralph
Jangle
Tinsel
Holly
Snowflake

LOTTIE: I hate making toys!

RALPH: Me, too!

LOTTIE: This is work!

RALPH: It's not fun at all!

LOTTIE: Let's get out of here!

RALPH: OK!

(RALPH and LOTTIE turn to leave. JANGLE enters.)

JANGLE: Stop right there. Where are you going?

LOTTIE: We are leaving!

(TINSEL, HOLLY, and SNOWFLAKE enter.)

TINSEL: Did someone say, "We are leaving"?

RALPH: Yes!

HOLLY: No!

SNOWFLAKE: How shocking!

JANGLE: No elf has ever left Santa's workshop.

LOTTIE: You don't even pay us!

RALPH: And we're not elves!

(JANGLE, TINSEL, HOLLY, and SNOWFLAKE gasp.)

SNOWFLAKE: You look like elves.

HOLLY: You sound like elves.

TINSEL: You smell like elves.

RALPH/LOTTIE: But we are not elves!

JANGLE: I knew it!

TINSEL: No, you didn't.

JANGLE: Yes, I did!

RALPH: So are we fired?

JANGLE: Yes!

LOTTIE: OK. Let's go.

HOLLY: You can't go.

SNOWFLAKE: You know the secrets of Santa's workshop.

TINSEL: You can't leave.

RALPH: Are you gonna . . . kill us?

HOLLY: No, we are not going to kill you. Are we?

JANGLE: No. We will just hold you prisoner forever.

RALPH: But I wanna go home to my mommy!

LOTTIE: We promise we won't tell any secrets. Let us go!

TINSEL: On second sniff, they do not smell like elves. I think we should let them go home.

JANGLE: But—our secrets!

SNOWFLAKE: No one will believe them.

HOLLY: Their friends will laugh at them.

JANGLE: Let me think.

(JANGLE walks around LOTTIE and RALPH while he thinks.)

JANGLE: You are children.

RALPH/LOTTIE: Yes!

JANGLE: Not elves.

RALPH/LOTTIE: Yes!

JANGLE: I think they will get too big to fit into the jail. We have to let them go.

RALPH/LOTTIE: Hooray!

SNOWFLAKE: This was the strangest Christmas
ever!

Questions

1. Do you think Ralph and Lottie's mother misses
them?

2. How did Ralph and Lottie get to the North Pole?

3. Should the elves let the children go?

4. Do you think Lottie and Ralph will tell their
friends and family about working in Santa's
workshop?

5. Do you think anyone would believe Lottie and
Ralph's story?

6. How do you think they will get home?

7. Will they get in trouble when they get home?

8. Will they ever go back to Santa's workshop?

ENDING 3: LOTTIE AND RALPH RAISE THE ROOF

Lottie and Ralph get too big for Santa's workshop.

Characters

Lottie
Ralph
Sparkle
Twinky-Twinkle

LOTTIE: Another beautiful day in Santa's workshop.

RALPH: Can you believe we've been here for three years?

(SPARKLE and TWINKY-TWINKLE run in.)

SPARKLE: Oooo—look!

TWINKY-TWINKLE: Candy canes for breakfast!

(SPARKLE and TWINKY-TWINKLE give LOTTIE and RALPH mini-candy canes.)

RALPH/LOTTIE: Yeah!

(RALPH and LOTTIE both jump up and hit their heads on the ceiling.)

RALPH/LOTTIE: Ouch!

TWINKY-TWINKLE: You two are sure getting big.

RALPH: No, we're not.

SPARKLE: Yes, you are.

LOTTIE: Maybe your eyes are just getting big.

SPARKLE: That doesn't make sense.

TWINKY-TWINKLE: Look how little the candy canes look in your hands.

SPARKLE: My candy cane fell off the table today and almost crushed me!

TWINKY-TWINKLE: It took twenty-seven elves to lift it off of him!

RALPH: Maybe we got the smallest ones.

SPARKLE: *(To LOTTIE.)* And yesterday you made a hole in the roof when you raised your hand in elf-school!

LOTTIE: It was an accident!

TWINKY-TWINKLE: Are you sure you're elves?

LOTTIE: Yes!

RALPH: No.

LOTTIE: Ralph!

SPARKLE: We think you are humans.

LOTTIE: Humans? Don't be silly!

TWINKY-TWINKLE: Everyone thinks you are humans.

RALPH: Everyone?

TWINKY-TWINKLE: Santa knows you are humans. He's a human, too.

RALPH: Maybe I can be Santa!

SPARKLES: You can't be Santa!

RALPH: Why not?

SPARKLES: Santa is a magic human.

RALPH: Oh. Right.

LOTTIE: What if we built another workshop, big enough for humans?

RALPH: We could work there!

TWINKY-TWINKLE: That sounds OK.

RALPH/LOTTIE: Hooray!

RALPH: This is our tallest Christmas ever!

Questions

1. Should Lottie and Ralph go back to living with humans?

2. Do you think Ralph will ever become Santa?

3. Should the elves kick Lottie and Ralph out of the North Pole?

4. Why doesn't Santa make the children leave if he knows they are humans?

5. Why do Ralph and Lottie stay for three years in the North Pole?

6. Should Ralph and Lottie get a workshop all to themselves?

7. What would happen if you ate candy canes for breakfast?

ENDING 4: LOOTING LOTTIE

Lottie wants a toy of her very own.

Characters

Ralph
Lottie
Flurry
Ice
Hail

RALPH: I love making toys all day.

LOTTIE: Don't you ever wish you could have one of them?

RALPH: What do you mean?

LOTTIE: We build toys all day, but we never get to play with them.

RALPH: Sure we do. We have to make sure they all work.

LOTTIE: But don't you wish you could take one or two home?

RALPH: I don't need to take toys home. I play with them all day.

LOTTIE: Sometimes I wish some of them could be mine and no one else's.

RALPH: But we make them for other children.

LOTTIE: I know! And it's not fair. I don't get any
toys on Christmas.

RALPH: I love getting no toys on Christmas!

LOTTIE: What?

RALPH: I look at toys all year long. I love not
looking at toys on Christmas day!

LOTTIE: Ralph? I think you might be crazy.

RALPH: I think you might be crazy, Lottie.

(FLURRY enters.)

FLURRY: Ralph, we need your help in the video
games.

RALPH: OK!

(RALPH and FLURRY exit.)

LOTTIE: I want a toy for my very own. One that I
don't have to give away or share with anyone
else.

*(LOTTIE walks over to a toy on a table. She
reaches out to take it. ICE enters.)*

ICE: Hi, Lottie!

LOTTIE: *(Pulling her hand back.)* Oh! Hello, Ice!

ICE: What are you doing?

LOTTIE: Nothing.

ICE: You shouldn't steal.

LOTTIE: I wasn't! I was just looking.

ICE: Oh. OK. I guess I'll see you later.

LOTTIE: OK.

> (ICE exits. LOTTIE reaches out and grabs the toy, hiding it under her clothes. HAIL enters.)

HAIL: What did you just do?

LOTTIE: Nothing.

HAIL: You stole a toy! I saw you!

LOTTIE: No, I didn't.

HAIL: You hid it under your clothes!

LOTTIE: Ice told you!

HAIL: No, I saw you. You are in big trouble. You're going to get kicked out of Santa's workshop forever.

LOTTIE: Don't tell!

HAIL: I have to.

LOTTIE: No!

> (RALPH, ICE, and FLURRY enter.)

FLURRY: What's going on?

HAIL: Lottie stole a toy from that table!

ICE: I told you not to steal!

RALPH: Lottie, what's wrong with you?

LOTTIE: I'm sorry! I couldn't help it! I wanted a toy of my own!

FLURRY: But, Lottie, did you see who that toy was for?

LOTTIE: No.

FLURRY: Look at it!

(LOTTIE *pulls out the toy.*)

LOTTIE: It says, "To Lottie, From Flurry."

ICE: It was for you all along!

LOTTIE: I feel so silly! Thank you, Flurry.

HAIL: This was your luckiest Christmas ever!

Questions

1. Should Lottie still be kicked out of Santa's workshop for stealing?

2. Can you understand how Lottie feels?

3. Do you think you would want to steal a toy?

4. Do you think you'd be sick of toys if you worked in Santa's toy shop?

5. Do you think Lottie will still get in trouble?

6. What does looting mean?

ON THE WAY TO THE AGORA . . .

*Three children meet up with strange and
unusual creatures from ancient Greece.*

Characters

Domestica
Yiannis
Andromeda
Odysseus
Siren
Aphrodite
Cyclops

DOMESTICA: Let's see . . . We need grapes, dates,
cheese, and fish from the agora.

YIANNIS: Can we go now?

DOMESTICA: Yes, let's go. Hurry up, Andromeda.

*(DOMESTICA, YIANNIS, and ANDROMEDA
all take one big step. ODYSSEUS, a Greek
warrior and hero, pops in immediately.)*

ODYSSEUS: Stop!

ANDROMEDA: What's wrong?

ODYSSEUS: Nothing's wrong. Something is right!

DOMESTICA: What is it?

ODYSSEUS: Young man, have you ever dreamed of going to war? Defeating enemies? Sailing across the seas in search of adventure?

YIANNIS: Yes!

ODYSSEUS: Well, it just so happens that I am looking for a few good men to go to war with me in Troy.

DOMESTICA: Wait a minute! He is just a boy!

YIANNIS: I am not! Let's go, mister!

DOMESTICA: You don't even know who he is!

ODYSSEUS: Silly me. I thought everyone knew me. I am the great warrior Odysseus.

ANDROMEDA: So? You don't look so great.

ODYSSEUS: Well, I am.

YIANNIS: And I'm going!

DOMESTICA: No, you're not. We need to go to the agora and get food for dinner. So long, mister!

ODYSSEUS: Aw, rats!

(ODYSSEUS exits.)

YIANNIS: You are no fun, Domestica.

DOMESTICA: And you are not old enough to go to war, Yiannis.

YIANNIS: You think you're the boss of me, just because you are the oldest.

DOMESTICA: Let's go.

(DOMESTICA, YIANNIS, and ANDROMEDA all take one big step. SIREN pops in immediately.)

SIREN: Don't move a muscle. I'm looking for Andromeda.

ANDROMEDA: I'm Andromeda.

SIREN: I've heard things about you.

ANDROMEDA: I didn't do it.

SIREN: Are you sure?

ANDROMEDA: Sure, I'm sure.

SIREN: Too bad. I'm a siren. We are awesome singers who lure men into the ocean with our beautiful singing voices. We're looking for a new soloist.

ANDROMEDA: Oh! Well, in that case, I did do it. I love to sing!

SIREN: I heard you're really good. Want to join our group?

ANDROMEDA: Bye, guys. Nice knowing you.

DOMESTICA: Hold on here. Miss Siren, what happens after you lure the men into the ocean?

SIREN: They drown and sometimes we eat them.

YIANNIS: Gross!

DOMESTICA: No, thank you. Andromeda is coming with us to do some shopping at the agora.

SIREN: Have it your way.

(SIREN exits.)

ANDROMEDA: This stinks!

DOMESTICA: Come on. We have to get to the agora or Mom won't be able to make dinner.

(DOMESTICA, YIANNIS, and ANDROMEDA all take one big step. APHRODITE pops in immediately.)

APHRODITE: Hello, beautiful people!

YIANNIS: Ewww. A girl.

DOMESTICA: A goddess!

ANDROMEDA: A girlie goddess.

APHRODITE: I am Aphrodite, the goddess of love!

YIANNIS: Ewww. Love.

ANDROMEDA: She's wearing pink.

DOMESTICA: She's beautiful.

APHRODITE: You must be Domestica.

DOMESTICA: Yes, I am!

APHRODITE: Domestica, I have heard tales of your loyalty and your willingness to do the dishes for you mother.

DOMESTICA: You have?

APHRODITE: It just so happens that I need a dishwasher on Mount Olympus.

DOMESTICA: You do?

YIANNIS: Ewww. I hate doing dishes.

APHRODITE: I know. You think only of war.

ANDROMEDA: Domestica, are you actually thinking about going with her?

DOMESTICA: She is a goddess! And I would get to live on Mount Olympus with all the gods.

ANDROMEDA: And you would wash dishes! That's no fun.

APHRODITE: You are only interested in fun.

ANDROMEDA: That's right.

DOMESTICA: Here's the grocery list. Go to the agora. Hurry up, it's getting dark.

YIANNIS: Where are you going?

DOMESTICA: Mount Olympus, of course!

ANDROMEDA: If I don't get to sing with the Sirens and Yiannis doesn't get to go to war, there's no way that you can go to Mount Olympus.

DOMESTICA: It's not the same. You two are going to kill people. I am going to wash dishes.

YIANNIS: Do you hear yourself? That sounds awful.

ANDROMEDA: Mom needs you at home.

YIANNIS: I guess we all need you. We would never get to the agora without you.

ANDROMEDA: I'd goof around, and Yiannis would play with his slingshot.

DOMESTICA: That's true.

APHRODITE: But I am a goddess!

DOMESTICA: That's true, too.

YIANNIS: If you go, I go!

ANDROMEDA: If you go, I go, too!

(SIREN and ODYSSEUS enter.)

SIREN: Come with me, Andromeda.

ODYSSEUS: We sail the seven seas, Yiannis!

DOMESTICA: No! No! You are right. I need to stay at home and be with my family.

APHRODITE/ODYSSEUS/SIREN: Awwwww.

DOMESTICA: Now let's go.

(DOMESTICA, YIANNIS, and ANDROMEDA all take one big step. A huge one-eyed CYCLOPS pops in immediately.)

CYCLOPS: Where is the agora?

DOMESTICA/ANDROMEDA/YIANNIS: *(Pointing toward ODYSSEUS, SIREN, and APHRODITE.)* That way!

YIANNIS: It sure is hard living in Ancient Greece.

DOMESTICA: Let's go!

ANDROMEDA: For once, you don't have to tell me twice!

(YIANNIS, ANDROMEDA, and DOMESTICA exit.)

CYCLOPS: What's their problem?

ODYSSEUS: They have to get to the agora.

CYCLOPS: Well, they're going the wrong way.

Questions

1. Would you be tempted to go with Odysseus, the Siren, or Aphrodite? Why or why not?

2. What is an agora?

3. The ancient Greeks told lots of stories about gods and goddesses, monsters, and strange creatures. Why do you think they made up these stories?

4. How were the ancient Greeks different from us? How were they similar?

5. Do you think having a family is important? Why?

6. How can you act like brothers and sisters when you are not?

7. With a costume, how can you create a one-eyed, giant Cyclops?

8. How can you make Aphrodite look like a goddess? How do you think she walks and talks?

9. How can you make Odysseus look and act like a warrior?

10. What do you think a Siren looks like? What kind of an attitude does the Siren have?

LOST

Wally gets lost in the African jungle.

Characters

Wally
Yum Yum

An empty stage except for a large pot.

WALLY: *(Breathless and upset.)* I was on an African safari with my folks. I wandered away to chase a monkey, and now I'm lost in the jungle!

YUM YUM: *(Popping up from behind a bush.)* Ugh!

WALLY: Oh! Do you speak English?

YUM YUM: Yum Yum speak little bit English like Reverend Jones teach. He missionary here.

WALLY: Reverend Jones sounds like a good man. May I speak with Reverend Jones?

YUM YUM: Can't speak with Reverend Jones. He good, goooooood man. Good with yams and candied grubs.

WALLY: That's funny! You made it sound like you . . . No. You didn't eat Reverend Jones, d-d-did you?

YUM YUM: Yes. Ate him. GOOOOD man. He tell us to eat him.

WALLY: That's crazy! Nobody would say, "Hey, why don't you eat me for dinner tonight."

YUM YUM: He say, "Yum Yum, don't eat dirt. You are what you eat." Yum Yum want to be like Reverend Jones, so I eat him.

WALLY: Listen here—I'm not good. I'm a bad boy. I wandered away from my parents when they told me not to. So don't eat me! *(Starts to panic.)* Mommy! Daddy! Where are you? HELP! I'll never disobey again. MOMMYYYY!

YUM YUM: *(In a tough-guy Brooklyn accent.)* Take it easy, kid. I was just messin' wit cha. Ya walked onto our movie set and jumped in the middle of my big scene. *(Shouting to someone offstage.)* Yo, Jonesy! Phone da cops and report a missin' kid, will ya?

WALLY: That was mean. You really scared me.

YUM YUM: Sorry, kid. I was like gettin' into the acting thing and got carried away.

WALLY: So, you actually have telephones way out here in the jungle?

YUM YUM: Yeah. Sometimes we have to stand on an elephant to get good reception, though.

WALLY: Hey, can I pretend to be a cannibal with you while I wait for my parents to come get me?

YUM YUM: *(Pulling out a lollipop.)* Here, kid. Have a lollipop and sit over there. Keep your mouth shut while we finish makin' our movie. You're ruinin' everythin'!

Questions

1. Have you ever been sorry you didn't listen to your parents? When and why?

2. Do you think Yum Yum was a nice man? Why or why not?

3. What's a safari? Would you like to go on one? Have you been on one?

4. What is a missionary?

5. Can you act just like someone else you know— your teacher, your dog, a baby? Can you act just like you are in a strange place like the jungle or crossing a busy street or walking a tightrope in the circus? Can you make yourself believe you are truly there?

THE THING IN THE GARAGE

A Pick-an-Adventure Play.

THE BEGINNING: THE DISCOVERY

Sara and Billy discover a strange object in their garage. What is it?

Characters

Sara
Billy
Mom

SARA: What's this?

BILLY: What's what?

SARA: This big machine! In the garage!

BILLY: I don't know. I've never seen it before.

SARA: How did it get here?

BILLY: Maybe Dad made it.

SARA: Dad is an artist; he doesn't build big things like this.

BILLY: Maybe it's a spaceship!

SARA: Do you think so?

BILLY: It could be.

SARA: Do you think there are aliens inside?

BILLY: Maybe.

SARA: Do you think they're nice or mean?

BILLY: How do I know?

SARA: Should we . . . look inside?

BILLY: You ask a lot of questions!

SARA: I don't know what to do! Should we tell Mom and Dad?

MOM: What are you two up to?

BILLY/SARA: Nothing!

MOM: (*Entering.*) Come inside. It's time for lunch!

SARA: Just a minute!

MOM: Don't play in the garage. It's so messy; you could get hurt. (*Exits.*)

SARA: OK.

BILLY: Mom doesn't want us in here.

SARA: She's afraid something will fall on us.

BILLY: Or maybe she knows something about this!

SARA: Mom?

BILLY: Why not?

SARA: Mom is a spaceman? Spacegirl?

BILLY: Let's meet back here after dinner. We need to get to the bottom of this!

Questions

1. What do you think the thing in the garage is?

2. Do you believe in aliens? If so, do you think they are nice or mean?

3. Do you think Billy and Sara should be playing in the garage?

Pick an Adventure!

What happens next? You decide on the ending! Choose which scene ends the story.

Ending 1: The thing in the garage is a spaceship, and Mom is a space alien. For this ending, go to page 181.

Ending 2: The thing in the garage is a time machine, and Billy and Sara travel to the past. For this ending, go to page 187.

Ending 3: The thing in the garage is a time machine, and Billy and Sara travel to the future. For this ending, go to page 191.

Ending 4: The thing in the garage is a piece of art made by Billy and Sara's father. For this ending, go to page 195.

Want another ending? Draw or write it here!

ENDING 1: MY MOTHER FROM THE PLANET BLUPERT

Sara and Billy learn some strange news about their mother.

Characters
Billy
Sara
Mom

BILLY: Mom and Dad are watching TV. Now's our chance to find out what this thing is!

SARA: OK. You open the door.

BILLY: You open the door!

SARA: Why should I? It was your idea.

BILLY: It was my idea to come out here; it was your idea to open the door!

SARA: How else are we going to find out what this is?

BILLY: I don't know!

SARA: You're older.

BILLY: Fine! I'll do it. *(Opens the door.)*

SARA: What do you see?

BILLY: A lot of controls and buttons.

SARA: Touch them! See what happens.

BILLY: Are you crazy?

MOM: *(Entering.)* What did I tell you two about coming out here?

BILLY: Ummm, you said not to.

MOM: Right. Get out of there right now!

BILLY: OK. Sorry. Am I in trouble now?

MOM: You most certainly are!

SARA: Mom?

MOM: Yes?

SARA: Mom, do you . . . ? Is this . . . ?

MOM: Yes?

BILLY: Is this thing yours?

MOM: What thing?

SARA: That really big thing in the garage!

MOM: Oh, that. That's nothing.

BILLY: It's a really big thing with buttons inside and a control panel—

MOM: I told you not to go in there! Oh, well. I guess I may as well tell you now.

SARA: Tell us what?

MOM: You need to promise to keep this to yourself. This is top-secret information.

BILLY: OK! I like top-secret information!

SARA: OK.

MOM: Well, you see, I am not from around here.

SARA: You used to live on a farm!

MOM: Sort of.

BILLY: You are from Ohio!

MOM: Not exactly. I am from the planet Blupert.

BILLY/SARA: What?!

MOM: The planet Blupert.

SARA: I never heard about that planet in school.

MOM: It hasn't been discovered yet by scientists on Earth.

BILLY: Are you kidding? Is this a joke just to keep us out of the garage?

MOM: No, Billy. This is the truth.

BILLY: You're a space alien?

MOM: Well, yes.

BILLY: How come you're not green? And dripping goo?

MOM: Not all space aliens are like that.

BILLY: Can you change shape?

SARA: Billy! Mom, this is scaring me.

MOM: There's no need to be afraid. I am the same old mom you always knew. And, yes, Billy, I can change shape.

BILLY: Cool!

SARA: What's your real shape like?

MOM: My real shape is invisible.

SARA: Like a ghost?

MOM: Yes! It's actually very nice. It's like being the wind.

BILLY: Awesome! Can we change shape, too?

MOM: I don't know.

SARA: Are you our real mother?

MOM: Yes, of course!

BILLY: Is Dad an alien, too?

MOM: No. Dad is an artist.

SARA: Does he know that you're from space?

MOM: Yes. He thinks it's interesting, and he loves me for who I am.

BILLY: Weird.

SARA: Billy! Mom, why are you here? Are you going to go back to space?

MOM: You are my family. I'm going to stay here forever.

BILLY: Then why do you have a spaceship?

MOM: In a spaceship, I can go to the store and back in two seconds.

BILLY: Whoa! Can we go to the store now? Please, please?

MOM: Now you have to do your homework.

(SARA sneaks behind the spaceship.)

BILLY: I want to go to the store in the spaceship!

MOM: Billy, homework first. Maybe another day.

BILLY: But I want to do this now!

MOM: Let's go, young man. You too, Sara. *(Beat.)* Sara? Sara? Where did she go?

BILLY: Sara!

MOM: Maybe she's back in the house. Let's go, Billy.

SARA *(Voice only.)*: Being invisible is very nice! I'm glad I'm an alien!

Questions

1. Would you want to be invisible? What would you do if you were invisible?

2. Do you think it is easy for Mom to tell Billy and Sara her secret?

3. Would you marry an alien?

4. How would you react if your mother told you she was from outer space? Act our your reaction.

ENDING 2: THE MIDDLE AGES

Sara and Billy go back in time.

Characters

Billy
Sara
Woman

BILLY: Let's check this thing out!

SARA: What do you think all these buttons do?

BILLY: I don't know. Let's try some!

SARA: *(Poking some buttons.)* Twelve ninety-five.
Enter.

(BILLY and SARA start shaking and swaying.)

BILLY: Whoa! What did you do?

SARA: I don't know. I just pressed some buttons,
like you said to do!

(The shaking stops.)

BILLY: Whew. What was that?

SARA: Let's get out.

BILLY: Yeah.

(BILLY and SARA get out.)

SARA: Where's the house? I don't see it anymore.

BILLY: I just see grass and dirt.

(A WOMAN enters in rags.)

WOMAN: Let's go! If you don't get your farming work done, your father and I won't share the potato with you!

SARA: What?

WOMAN: What are you wearing? Did you steal these strange garments? If you did, you'll get your hands chopped off. Then you won't be any good to this family!

BILLY: We didn't steal these clothes!

SARA: I don't want to get my hands chopped off!

WOMAN: Then you'd better get these clothes dirty! Get to work!

BILLY: And when we're done, we'll get potatoes? I want French fries.

WOMAN: What? We don't have any French things here. They are our enemies! Keep your voice down!

BILLY: *(Whispering.)* We can't have French fries?

WOMAN: What are you talking about? When you are done your work, the whole family will share a potato. Just like every other day.

SARA: How big is our family?

WOMAN: I know we never taught you to read or write, but we did teach you to count to ten! You have six other brothers and sisters. So there are eight of us in the family.

BILLY: And we're sharing a potato?

WOMAN: I think your head is turning into a potato. *(Shouting.)* OR IS YOUR HEARING GOING LIKE UNCLE RICHARD??

BILLY: I can hear you just fine!

WOMAN: Then get to work! *(Exits.)*

SARA: Let's get out of here!

BILLY: We must be in a different time and place. Do you remember how you got us here?

SARA: I pressed some numbers here.

BILLY: Well, punch in the numbers of this year so we can get home!

SARA: *(Punching in some numbers.)* Cross your fingers!

(BILLY and SARA start shaking.)

BILLY: Here we go!

Questions

1. Would you like to go back to the past? Why or why not?

2. If you went back to the past, what time and place would you like to visit?

3. How could you pretend to have a time machine onstage (with no special effects)?

4. How do you think the Woman should be dressed?

ENDING 3: MIDDLE-AGED

Sara and Billy go forward in time.

Characters

Sara
Billy
Joe

SARA: What would happen if I press some numbers on this board here?

BILLY: I don't know. Probably nothing.

SARA: Two. Zero. Five. Zero.

(SARA and BILLY jerk back and forth, then come to a stop.)

BILLY: That was strange. Was there an earthquake?

SARA: Should we go outside?

BILLY: Sure.

(SARA and BILLY step outside. JOE enters.)

JOE: Hello, honey.

SARA: Are you talking to me?

JOE: Yes, of course I'm talking to you, Sara.

SARA: How do you know me?

JOE: I'm your husband.

SARA: I don't have a husband.

JOE: Ha ha ha. Come on inside. The kids are waiting for you to make dinner.

SARA: Make dinner? I'm not allowed to touch the stove.

JOE: You sure are funny tonight. Come on. We've all starving.

BILLY: Yeah, go on, Sara. Time to cook dinner with your husband.

SARA: Shut up! Don't be gross!

BILLY: You're the one who got married!

JOE: So how are the elephants, Billy?

BILLY: The elephants?

JOE: What is it with you two tonight? Always joking around. The elephants, Billy. The ones you clean up after.

BILLY: I clean up after elephants?

JOE: You work at the zoo. You clean out the elephant area. Hope the big shovel we bought you for Christmas is working out.

BILLY: I scoop up elephant doo?

JOE: If you don't, you'll get fired.

(SARA laughs.)

BILLY: Be quiet, Sara! At least I'm not married!

JOE: I'm very confused. I'm going inside. I hope you two will be in soon so we can celebrate Billy's fiftieth birthday.

BILLY: WHAT?!

SARA: You're old, Billy!

BILLY: If I'm old, then you're old, too!

SARA: Let's get outta here!

(SARA and BILLY run back to the time machine.)

BILLY: I'm definitely going to do my homework now! I don't want to clean up after elephants!

SARA: And I'm never talking to a boy for as long as I live!

Questions

1. What do you think your future will be like when you're fifty?

2. What do you think the world will be like when you're fifty? How will it be different than it is today?

3. What are three goals you have for when you're older?

ENDING 4: ART?

Sara and Billy do not like their father's new art project.

Characters

Sara
Dad
Billy

SARA: Shh! We need to be quiet so we don't get—

DAD: Hello!

BILLY: Dad! What are you doing in here?

DAD: What am I doing in here? I'm working!

SARA: Did Mom tell you to clean out the garage?

DAD: She probably did. But that's not what I'm doing!

BILLY: What are you doing?

DAD: Can't you tell?

SARA: You're building a spaceship?

BILLY: Creating a time machine?

DAD: Is that what this looks like to you? Hmmm . . . interesting.

SARA: What are you doing?

DAD: I'm making art, of course!

BILLY/SARA: Art?

DAD: Isn't it beautiful?

BILLY: Um . . .

SARA: Sure.

BILLY: I thought you were a painter.

DAD: I was! Then I got this wonderful idea!

SARA: What is it supposed to be?

DAD: It's a skunk sitting on a cow's head.

SARA: It is?

BILLY: Are you sure?

DAD: Well, it's not finished yet. It's going to be beautiful. People are going to pay a lot of money for this!

SARA: Excuse us, Dad. Billy and I need to talk over here for a minute.

DAD: OK!

(SARA and BILLY step away.)

SARA: Billy, this is terrible! Dad is never going to sell that thing in the garage!

BILLY: I know! It doesn't look like a cow or a skunk!

SARA: We have to get him to go back to painting.

BILLY: How?

SARA: I don't know. But we have to try.

(SARA and BILLY go back to the garage.)

BILLY: Dad, I have a great idea. Why don't you paint a cow with a skunk on its head?

DAD: Why would I paint it? I am making this beautiful sculpture.

SARA: Everyone is always saying what a great painter you are.

DAD: That's very nice!

BILLY: Mom is always saying she loves your paintings.

DAD: Mm-hm.

(Beat. SARA and BILLY don't know what to do.)

SARA: Dad, this thing is not pretty!

DAD: Oh!

SARA: I'm sorry, I didn't mean to hurt your feelings, but we thought you should know.

BILLY: Sara thought you should know. I thought you were OK not knowing.

SARA: Billy!

DAD: No, that's OK. You don't have to like everything I do.

SARA: But, Dad, what if nobody buys this?

DAD: I'm just trying something new. If it doesn't work out, that's OK.

SARA: It is?

DAD: Sure. It's good to try new things.

BILLY: I think I'm going to try not doing my homework.

DAD: I don't think so. In fact, I think you two should go inside and do your homework now!

SARA: Thanks a lot, Billy.

Questions

1. Do you think it was a good idea for Sara to tell her dad that she didn't like his sculpture?

2. How is a sculpture different from a painting?

3. Do you think it's a good idea to try new things, even if you don't succeed?

4. What's one new thing you would like to try?

5. How do Billy and Sara try to convince their dad to go back to painting? What other methods could they try?

THE BIRTHDAY GIFT

A Pick-an-Adventure Play.

THE BEGINNING: ROGER WANTS A PET

Roger wants a pet from Jupiter.

Characters
Mom
Roger
Dad

MOM: What do you want for your birthday, Roger?

ROGER: I want to have a picnic on Jupiter. And I want to find a pet on Jupiter and bring it home.

DAD: Roger, I'm not sure you're old enough to take care of a pet.

ROGER: Dad! Please?

DAD: Maybe we can go to Jupiter and see how things go.

ROGER: Things are gonna go great!

MOM: Would you like to bring a friend?

ROGER: I'm new to Earth. I don't have any friends. That's why I need a pet!

MOM: You have to try to make friends here.

ROGER: I had lots of great friends on Mercury.

MOM: All that heat wasn't good for your father's health.

ROGER: The only person you care about is Dad!

MOM: Don't be silly.

DAD: You know that's not true, Roger.

ROGER: So can I please get a pet for my birthday?

MOM: You heard your father. We'll see.

DAD: Don't get your hopes up. You're too young for a pet.

ROGER: I am not!

Pick an Adventure!

What happens next? You decide on the ending!
Choose which scene ends the story.

Ending 1: Roger doesn't get a pet. For this ending,
go to page 203.

Ending 2: Roger gets a pet. For this ending, go to
page 207.

Want another ending? Draw or write it here!

ENDING 1: ROGER MAKES A FRIEND/ROGER LOSES A FRIEND

Roger goes to his first playground on the planet Earth.

Characters

Roger
Mom
Henry

ROGER: Another day on Earth with no friends or even a pet.

MOM: Roger, our neighbor told me that place next door is called a playground. It's a place for Earth children to play. They sit on boards tied to trees, fly back and forth, and push each other. At least, that's what she told me.

ROGER: Wow! That sounds like even more fun than Mercury. I get to push other kids—cool!

(ROGER and MOM hold hands and walk next door to the imaginary playground.)

MOM: I'll let you play here until dinnertime, Roger. Here's a nice red plum for you, just in case you get hungry.

(MOM waves good-bye and exits.)

ROGER: No one's even paying attention to me. I'll never find a friend. Maybe this plum could be my pet. Hi, little plum! Your name is Red. You are my new pet and my favorite buddy. Let's sit on this rock together and watch the other kids. *(Beat.)* Isn't this fun! Let's play like the Earth kids. I'll push you.

(ROGER pushes the plum off the rock as HENRY approaches, holding a blue ball.)

HENRY: Hi! You're the new kid who moved into the yellow house, right?

ROGER: Yep. What are you holding—your pet?

HENRY: Very funny. No, it's my new blue ball. Do you want to play catch?

ROGER: *(Standing.)* Sure. Should I push you first?

HENRY: Ha-ha. You're weird, but I like you. Here—catch!

(HENRY throws the ball to ROGER. ROGER throws the ball back.)

ROGER: That was fun! What's your name?

HENRY: Henry. What's yours?

ROGER: My name is Roger. I gotta go home for dinner now, Henry. Can we play catch again tomorrow?

HENRY: Sure—it's great to have a new friend.

ROGER: Oh, I just remembered! I left my new pet Red in the sun over there. I hope he's OK. I'd better go get him.

(ROGER and HENRY walk to the rock.)

HENRY: I don't see your pet, but someone left a prune back here. *(Pretends to pick up a prune.)*

ROGER: Oh no! Red! What happened to you?

HENRY: Yum! *(Henry pretends to eat a prune.)* I just can't get enough prunes!

ROGER: Oh well. I guess it's better to have a regular friend.

Questions

1. Have you ever been the new kid in your neigh-borhood or class? If yes, how did it feel? If no, how do you think it might feel?

2. Can you think of ways that a person can make a new friend?

3. What does a grape become when it's left in the sun?

4. What happened to Roger's plum?

ENDING 2: ROGER GETS A PET

Roger goes to Jupiter.

Characters

Mom
Woofie
Roger
Dad

MOM: Well, Roger, this has been quite a birthday for you. Here we are on Jupiter and you got Woofie, too.

DAD: Remember, son, you have to feed and brush your hound dog every day if you want a happy pet.

ROGER: You bet, Dad, and I'll walk him every day, too!

(WOOFIE howls. ROGER sighs.)

ROGER: That's thirty-five times.

DAD: Don't forget. It's much colder here on Jupiter than on Earth, so Woofie has to wear a sweater outside.

MOM: And really hold on to his leash because the winds outside are about 150 miles per hour.

ROGER: Mom, Dad, this vacation has been great, but I think I'm ready to go back to Earth and make some friends now.

(*WOOFIE howls. ROGER sighs.*)

ROGER: That's thirty-six times.

DAD: It seems like we just got here. Let's stay a little longer.

MOM: You're right, dear. Time does fly when you are on Jupiter! That's because the days are only ten hours long.

(*WOOFIE howls. ROGER sighs.*)

ROGER: That's thirty-seven. Please, please, Dad, let's leave today. Woofie likes to bark at the moon, and Jupiter has thirty-nine moons! It's driving me crazy.

MOM: Did you know that a person who weighs one hundred pounds on Earth weighs 236 pounds on Jupiter? Oh my. This place is not good for my self-esteem. Let's leave.

DAD: You know, I just got a note from Earth. There's a new president in the United States of America over in the Western Hemisphere. He wants me to build solar panels for renewable energy there.

MOM/ROGER: We're ready when you are!

(WOOFIE howls. ROGER sighs.)

ROGER: That's thirty-eight times!

DAD: OK, if we leave right now, we can stop for lunch on Mars and be back to Earth by dinnertime.

ROGER: Can we eat at McDonald's?

(WOOFIE howls. ROGER, MOM, and DAD sigh.)

ROGER/MOM/DAD: Thirty-nine!

Questions

1. Is Jupiter closer or further away from the sun than planet Earth?

2. What planet is between Jupiter and Earth in our solar system?

3. Could a boy really walk his dog on Jupiter? Why or why not?

4. How many moons do we have rotating around Earth?

5. How many moons rotate around Jupiter?

6. Would you like to travel to other planets? Why or why not?

THE DUEL

A Pick-an-Adventure Play.

THE BEGINNING: WENDELA CHALLENGES EDWARD

Wendela has challenged Edward to a magic duel. Will they fight to the "poof"?

Characters

Edward
Alistair
Wendela
Roberta
Denice
Professor Jackalope

DENICE and ROBERTA stand onstage right.

DENICE: Did you hear?

ROBERTA: Hear what?

DENICE: About the duel?

ROBERTA: The what?

DENICE: The duel! The magical duel!

ROBERTA: What's a duel?

(ALISTAIR runs in from the left, panicked.)

ALISTAIR: Did you hear? Did you hear? Edward and Wendela are going to fight!

ROBERTA: They're going to fight?

DENICE: That's what I've been trying to tell you! A duel is a fight!

ROBERTA: Well, why didn't you just say so?

ALISTAIR: But it's worse than just a regular old fight. Edward and Wendela are going to duel with magic. And I think they are going to try to make each other go poof!

ROBERTA: Poof?

ALISTAIR: Poof!

DENICE: They are going to try to make each other disappear.

ROBERTA: Why didn't you just say so?

ALISTAIR: Don't you see what this means? This is serious!

DENICE: Why do they want to make each other disappear?

ALISTAIR: Denice, she's called Wendela the Wicked. She just likes to do bad stuff! And she hates Edward.

ROBERTA: Edward is nice.

ALISTAIR: Exactly!

DENICE: Calm down, Alistair. Here comes Edward.
Maybe we can convince him not to fight.
Edward!

(EDWARD enters from stage right.)

EDWARD: Hi!

ALISTAIR: How can you be so calm right now?
Wendela is going to make you go poof!

ROBERTA: Here comes Wendela!

DENICE: You don't have to duel her, Edward.

EDWARD: Yes, I do. She is unkind to everyone. She
must be stopped.

ROBERTA: But are you going to make her go poof?

EDWARD: I don't want to make her disappear.
I just want to teach her a lesson.

ALISTAIR: But she wants to make you disappear!

DENICE: Edward, are you sure about this?

ROBERTA: She's here!

*(WENDELA confidently enters from stage left
and stands far away from the others.)*

WENDELA: It's time for our duel, Edward.

EDWARD: Very well.

DENICE: Is this really necessary?

WENDELA: Get out of the way, Denice.

EDWARD: Go on, Denice. This is between Wendela and me.

DENICE: Wendela, why do you hate Edward?

WENDELA: Edward is always good and he is always right and everyone likes Edward.

ROBERTA: So?

WENDELA: So, ridiculous Roberta, I do not like Edward because he is good and he is always right and everyone likes him!

ROBERTA: Why are you so wicked, Wendela?

WENDELA: Enough questions! Questions are boring. It is time to duel. Are you brave enough to face me, Edward?

EDWARD: I am not afraid of you.

WENDELA: You should be.

EDWARD: We begin!

ALISTAIR: Aaaaaaah!

(ALISTAIR runs offstage in a panic. ROBERTA and DENICE move back to get out of the way. WENDELA and EDWARD pull out their wands.)

Questions

1. When a play says "stage right," this is what it means: When an actor is facing the audience, stage right is their right. Stand and face your class (they are your audience) and move to stage left (your left).

2. If someone challenged you to a duel, would you do it or would you refuse? Would you be scared like Alistair?

3. What do you think it means to go "poof"?

Pick an Adventure!

What happens next? You decide on the ending!
Choose which scene ends the story.

Ending 1: Wendela puts a terrible spell on Edward.
For this ending, go to page 217.

Ending 2: Edward defeats Wendela. For this ending,
go to page 221.

Ending 3: Roberta discovers why Wendela is so
mean. For this ending, go to page 225.

Ending 4: Edward goes "poof!" and finds himself in
a new land. For this ending, go to page 229.

Want another ending? Draw or write it here!

ENDING 1: THE OLD SWITCHEROO

Edward and Wendela switch bodies.

Characters

Edward
Denice
Wendela
Roberta
Alistair
Professor Jackalope

EDWARD: Denice, will you give us the sign to begin?

DENICE: OK. One, two, three—magic!

(EDWARD and WENDELA flick their wands. WENDELA gets dizzy and stumbles around. EDWARD goes onto his hands and knees and snorts like a pig.)

ROBERTA: Shake it off, Edward!

(EDWARD and WENDELA both shake off their spells, becoming themselves again.)

WENDELA: Once more! One, two, three—magic!

(EDWARD and WENDELA flick their wands. Both jump back like they've been hit. Then nothing happens.)

ROBERTA: I think you guys missed.

EDWARD: Shut up, ridiculous Roberta. You know nothing!

ROBERTA: Edward, not you, too! Wendela made you mean!

WENDELA: Ah ha ha haaaa!

EDWARD: Oh no. I, Wendela, am in your stupid body, Edward.

WENDELA: And I'm a girl! A nasty, witchy girl!

(PROFESSOR JACKALOPE enters with ALISTAIR.)

PROFESSOR JACKALOPE: What's going on here?

EDWARD: Nothing!

ALISTAIR: They're dueling!

ROBERTA: That means they're fighting.

(PROFESSOR JACKALOPE walks over to WENDELA.)

PROFESSOR JACKALOPE: Did you start this, Wendela?

WENDELA: I'm Edward.

PROFESSOR JACKALOPE: Are you trying to be funny?

WENDELA: No! It's the truth! I'm Edward and she—he—over there in my body—is Wendela.

(PROFESSOR JACKALOPE walks over to EDWARD.)

PROFESSOR JACKALOPE: Wendela? Is that you?

EDWARD: Professor, I don't know why Wendela is telling lies about me.

PROFESSOR JACKALOPE: Wendela, come with me. This behavior is unacceptable!

(PROFESSOR JACKALOPE and WENDELA walk offstage. ALISTAIR walks up to EDWARD.)

ALISTAIR: Edward?

DENICE: Don't you see, Alistair? This is Wendela. She's in Edward's body.

ROBERTA: Ooooooh. I get it . . . I think.

EDWARD: This is going to be fun. Nice little Edward is going to do some very nasty things now.

ALISTAIR: Aaaaaaah!

(ALISTAIR runs offstage.)

Questions

1. What happened? What was the spell Wendela cast on Edward?

2. What will happen in the end? Will Edward and Wendela be switched back or will they stay in each other's bodies? Will they duel again? Will the spell wear off?

3. Will anyone discover what Wendela did?

4. What do you think Wendela is planning?

5. Do you think Wendela will like being in Edward's body?

6. Would you tell a teacher about a duel, like Alistair did?

7. How can you act out being dizzy or turning into a pig without special costumes?

8. How does Edward change when he becomes Wendela? How does Wendela change when she becomes Edward? Do their voices change? Do they stand or walk differently? Do they behave differently? Practice acting like both Edward and Wendela. See if you can tranform into both characters.

ENDING 2: WENDELA TAKES OVER

Wendela does something wicked!

Characters
Wendela
Edward
Denice
Roberta
Alistair

WENDELA: I have some bad news for you, Edward.

EDWARD: You're afraid to duel?

WENDELA: No. Something much, much worse.

DENICE: What is it?

WENDELA: I took over the school.

ROBERTA: What?

WENDELA: I am in charge now.

EDWARD: Impossible!

(ALISTAIR enters, panicking.)

ALISTAIR: You guys! Wendela turned Professor Jackalope into ice! He's melting!

DENICE: How can that be? Professor Jackalope is so powerful! How could Wendela defeat him?

ALISTAIR: She surprised him. Wendela snuck up behind him. His back was facing the door.

ROBERTA: That's not fair!

EDWARD: I've had enough of your evil ways, Wendela. I will defeat you once and for all!

(EDWARD throws a spell toward WENDELA. WENDELA ducks; the spell misses her completely.)

DENICE: Edward, don't get upset! Stay calm!

WENDELA: Are you upset because I put a spell on your favorite teacher? Or because I defeated the strongest wizard in history?

EDWARD: Enough! *(Throws a spell at WENDELA.)*

(WENDELA's mouth is stuck shut. She tries to pull it open, she shakes her head, she tries to scream, but her mouth stays shut.)

ROBERTA: Finally! I will never have to hear Wendela call me Ridiculous Rob—

(WENDELA throws a spell at ROBERTA, gluing her mouth shut. ROBERTA is very surprised and also tries to get her mouth open.)

ALISTAIR: Quick, Edward!

(EDWARD throws another spell at WENDELA, making her arms stick to her sides.)

EDWARD: Now you will never cast another spell!

DENICE: Free Roberta and let's go help Professor Jackalope!

(EDWARD releases ROBERTA from the spell.)

ROBERTA: Ahhhhh. That feels so much better!

ALISTAIR: What are you going to do with Wendela?

EDWARD: I will leave her for now. Professor Jackalope will know what to do with her.

ROBERTA: I think she should go poof!

ALISTAIR: I think she should be turned into a polar bear and be put on the North Pole!

DENICE: I think she should stay just as she is now.

EDWARD: I think she will probably go to jail for a long, long time. Hurry! Let's go save the professor!

Questions

1. Do you think Edward and his friends will save the day?

2. What will happen to Roberta?

3. What would it look like onstage to throw or cast a spell? Can you act it out?

4. Why do you think plays and movies have villains? How do villains help a story? What if there were no villains in plays and movies?

5. What does conflict mean? Where do you see conflict in this scene?

ENDING 3: WENDELA'S WISH

Roberta finds out why Wendela is not nice.

Characters
Roberta
Denice
Wendela
Edward
Alistair

ROBERTA: Wait! Don't duel yet. I want to know the answer to my question. Why are you so mean, Wendela?

DENICE: I think we'd all like to know that.

WENDELA: Talking is stupid. Let's duel!

EDWARD: Very well, let's duel! One, two, three—magic!

(WENDELA and EDWARD both cast spells.)

EDWARD: Ouch!

DENICE: Are you OK?

EDWARD: Yes. Roberta, ask your question again.

ROBERTA: Wendela, why are you so mean?

WENDELA: Nobody likes me. Nobody is nice to me. Everybody thinks I'm strange. It makes me sad and lonely. I hate seeing people laughing and talking to their friends! I'm not mean, you're the mean ones!

(ALISTAIR enters slowly and carefully.)

ALISTAIR: Is everybody OK?

DENICE: Wendela doesn't seem to be herself.

ROBERTA: What did you do to her, Edward?

EDWARD: I cast a truth spell on her. Now she will only tell the truth.

DENICE: Wendela, do you . . . want to be our friend?

WENDELA: Yes, but you don't like me.

ROBERTA: Do you think I'm ridiculous?

WENDELA: I think you are lucky. I am much smarter than you, and yet the other kids like you better. It's not fair!

ALISTAIR: That's because you're evil and scary.

DENICE: You should try being nicer.

WENDELA: I want to be nicer! Did I really say that? I don't like this truth spell!

EDWARD: You should be nicer. That's the way to make friends.

WENDELA: I don't know how to be nice.

ALISTAIR: Stop casting spells on people!

ROBERTA: Don't call people names.

DENICE: Be happy for other people instead of being jealous.

EDWARD: Let's call a truce. We will try to be nicer to you, and you will try to be nicer to us. OK?

WENDELA: Will you eat lunch with me?

ROBERTA: No way!

DENICE: Roberta, we're being nicer to each other, remember?

ROBERTA: But she's still so scary!

EDWARD: We have to try, too. Yes, you can have lunch with us.

ALISTAIR: Everyone will think we've gone crazy.

DENICE: Well, she is smart and clever. Maybe we can be friends. I'll try.

ROBERTA: Then I will, too.

ALISTAIR: Me, too!

EDWARD: So will I. Let's go get some fish sticks.

WENDELA: I'm going to turn mine into pizza.

ALISTAIR: She is clever!

(ALL exit.)

Questions

1. Why doesn't Wendela like Edward?

2. Why do you think Wendela is mean?

3. Do you think everyone will be friends now? Why or why not?

4. Do you think not having friends is an excuse for being a bully? Why or why not?

5. Would it be fair if Professor Jackalope put a truth spell on his students? Are there times when it might be good to have a truth spell?

ENDING 4: ZALA LAND

A spell puts Edward in another world.

Characters
Wendela
Denice
Roberta
Edward
Norp
Alistair

WENDELA: One, two, three—magic!

(EDWARD and WENDELA cast spells.)

DENICE: Oh no! Edward is . . .

ROBERTA: Going pooooooooooooooof!

(WENDELA, DENICE, and ROBERTA all fly offstage in slow motion. EDWARD is left alone.)

EDWARD: Where did everybody go? Where am I?

NORP: Who are you?

EDWARD: Who are you?

NORP: I am Norp.

EDWARD: I am Edward.

NORP: Ed-wid?

EDWARD: Edward.

NORP: What a strange name!

EDWARD: Your name is Norp!

NORP: Don't be jealous.

EDWARD: I'm not jealous. Where am I?

NORP: You're in Zala Land.

EDWARD: Is that in Africa?

NORP: What is Africa?

EDWARD: A place on planet Earth.

NORP: I have never been to Earth.

EDWARD: What planet is this?

NORP: Bibbil.

EDWARD: Planet Bibbil? How did I get here?

NORP: I don't know. Are you an Earthling?

EDWARD: Yes. I was dueling in school—This must be Wendela's spell!

NORP: Princess Wendela? Where is she? Her mother and father have been looking for her everywhere!

EDWARD: You know Wendela?

NORP: Everyone knows Wendela! She is the nicest person in the universe!

EDWARD: Wendela? Are you serious?

NORP: Of course I am serious! They are going to declare who is the nicest person in the universe later today. So everyone is looking all over for Wendela!

EDWARD: That is why she was trying to destroy me! She will certainly lose the competition now! Wait a minute . . . Wendela has been mean for many, many years! How can she be considered the nicest person in the universe? She calls people names, stomps on their feet, casts spells that turn people into frogs and pigs—

NORP: I know, I know! Could she be any nicer?

EDWARD: What does "nice" mean here?

NORP: Nice means calling people names, stomping on their feet, casting spells that turn people into frogs and pigs—

EDWARD: Then Wendela is sure to win that award.

NORP: But she had to cast one more big spell to be the clear winner. She is in close competition with Lalatobala of planet Ruchawaz.

EDWARD: That is why she wanted a duel! How do I get home now?

NORP: You want to go back to Earth?

EDWARD: Yes!

NORP: Are you sure?

EDWARD: Yes!

(*WENDELA enters.*)

WENDELA: I won!

NORP: I knew you would, Princess Wendela! You are the nicest person in the universe!

WENDELA: Which, of course, means I am the meanest person in the universe.

NORP: Of course.

EDWARD: Can I go home now?

WENDELA: No.

EDWARD: Why not?

WENDELA: I can't do anything good. They'll take away my award!

EDWARD: Come on. This isn't funny anymore.

WENDELA: No.

EDWARD: Please?

WENDELA: No!

EDWARD: If you don't send me back, I'll be here forever.

WENDELA: Ewww. Very well. But I can't do it. Norp, will you send him back to Earth?

NORP: OK.

EDWARD: You had the power to send me back to Earth all along?

NORP: Yes.

EDWARD: Why didn't you?

NORP: You didn't ask.

EDWARD: Yes, I did!

NORP: Oh yeah. Here you go . . .

(NORP blinks. WENDELA and NORP fly offstage in slow motion. DENICE, ROBERTA, and ALISTAIR fly onstage in slow motion.)

DENICE: There you are!

ROBERTA: We thought you went poof!

EDWARD: I just went to Zala Land.

ROBERTA: Oh.

ALISTAIR: Where is that?

EDWARD: On the planet Bibbil.

DENICE: We're glad you're back. What happened? You disappeared, then Wendela disappeared a few minutes later—

EDWARD: I don't think we'll be seeing Wendela again.

ROBERTA: Really?

EDWARD: She is from Zala Land. She was being so
mean to win an award there.

ALISTAIR: She's never coming back?

EDWARD: I don't think so.

DENICE: I think this calls for a celebration!

Questions

1. In a land where everything is backward, what would you be like? What qualities would you like best about yourself (that you might not like here on Earth)? What would you be ashamed of (that you are proud of here on Earth)?

2. How should Norp be different from the other children? Should Norp be different? How old is Norp? What do you think Norp does for a living?

3. Would you like to visit Zala Land? Why or why not?

4. This is the stage direction for when Edward goes poof: *(WENDELA, DENICE, and ROBERTA all fly offstage in slow motion. EDWARD is left alone.)* Can you act this out? How can you make it look strange and magical?

5. Do you have other ideas of how you can make Edward go poof without special effects?

6. Do you think Wendela will ever show up at school again?

ABOUT THE AUTHOR

Kristen Dabrowski is an actress, writer, acting teacher, and director. The actor's life has taken her all over the United States and England. Her other books, published by Smith and Kraus, include *My First Monologue Book; 111 Monologues for Middle School Actors; The Ultimate Audition Book for Teens 3, 11,* and *12; 20 Ten-Minute Plays for Teens;* the Teens Speak series; and the educational 10+ play series (six books, including two volumes for kids). Currently, she lives in the world's smallest apartment in New York City. You can contact the author at monologuemadness @yahoo.com.